REINHOLD PLASTICS APPLICATIONS SERIES

POLYAMIDE RESINS

by
DON E. FLOYD
General Mills, Inc.
Minneapolis, Minn.

REINHOLD PUBLISHING CORPORATION
NEW YORK
CHAPMAN & HALL, LTD., LONDON

Library of Congress Catalog Card Number: 58-7395

Printed in the United States of America
THE GUINN CO., INC.
New York 14, N. Y.

Reinhold Plastics Applications Series

Many factors are involved in the determination of the optimum application of a plastic and the correct application in a very real sense determines the true worth of a material. The plastic best to use for a given product must not only fill the required physical specifications, but it must also be competitively priced.

Realizing the importance of correct application in the whole gamut of plastics activity, the Reinhold Publishing Corporation, early in 1956, decided to publish a series of short books emphasizing the applications of the various types of commercial materials of the plastics industry—each book to cover one type of material or one process. The present volume by Donald E. Floyd is the third of this series. Those already published are the volumes on polyethylene and polyurethanes. Others now in preparation cover the following subjects: acrylics, cellulosics, epoxies, fluorocarbons, laminates, polystyrenes, gum plastics, silicones, vacuum forming, vinyls and welding of plastics.

The series is semi-technical—that is, one does not need to be a chemist to understand the various volumes. The authors have kept in mind as probable readers such industrial men and women as: design engineers, equipment manufacturers, producers of packages, manufacturers of packaging machinery, students at technical schools and, of course, those in the plastics industry—material manufacturers, molders, extruders, fabricators.

In addition to the above, it is hoped that each title will

appeal to readers in specialized categories. Plastics from which fibers are made may be of interest to tire and fabric manufacturers. A book such as the one on vinyls, which materials are favorable for production of sheets, may have value for manufacturers of handbags and luggage. Similarly, other titles may appeal to manufacturers of paints, recorder tapes, upholstery, plywood and furniture.

With this program now well launched, it is with enthusiasm that this third book of the series is presented.

HERBERT R. SIMONDS, *Editor*

Titles Published

PREFACE

The purpose of this book is to discuss the various important applications of the polymers belonging to the polyamide resin family. To accomplish this purpose it is necessary not only to classify the applications, but also to review what considerations and properties make the polyamide resins useful in these applications. In some instances, strength and toughness are the predominating factors, while in others it is specific adhesion, coefficient of friction, wear resistance, or tendency toward crystallinity. There has been an effort throughout the book to bring into perspective applications based on property evaluation.

In addition to relating properties and applications, this book tries to relate polyamide resin properties to resin composition and structure. The end result is that a rough relationship is established between application on the one hand and chemical composition and structure on the other for the various established types of polyamides.

An explanation of why certain polyamide resins are used in certain fields and what it is that makes them useful, makes possible predictions and discussion of trends for the future of the polyamide resin family. Development of new resins, effect of costs in competitive fields, and development of new uses for the resins are covered within separate chapters and in a summary chapter at the end of the book.

The author is grateful to General Mills for much help in preparation of the manuscript and especially for the services of the library, stenographic and drafting departments. Special acknowledgement is made to the valuable help of Miss June Whitney and Miss Karen Rose for typing and proofreading of the manuscript. The author is indebted to several companies for their kindness in donating photographs and data to be used in this volume. These include E. I. duPont de Nemours and Company, Societe Organico, Barrett Division of Allied Chemical and Dye Corporation and others. And, finally, the author is very grateful to Dr. Herbert R. Simonds for having suggested the idea of such a book and for the suggested outline of contents, and to Mr. A. C. Hopkins for his encouragement and his help in establishing contacts with others.

Research Laboratory
General Mills, Inc.
Minneapolis, Minnesota
June 9, 1957

CONTENTS

1. INTRODUCTION

In October, 1938, announcement was made of a group of new synthetic materials resembling silk and wool both in appearance and in chemical composition. This group, a member of the polyamide family, was given the generic name *nylon*.

The Du Pont Company's official definition of *nylon* is as follows: "A generic term for any long chain synthetic polymeric amide which has recurring amide groups as an integral part of the main polymer chain and which is capable of being formed into a filament in which the structural elements are oriented in the direction of the axis."

Work with polyamides was undertaken in 1928 by Du Pont's W. H. Carothers at the Experimental Station in Wilmington, Delaware. He studied the polymers obtainable from epsilon-aminocaproic acid and other amino acids capable of self-condensation to form linear polymers, as well as the reaction products of dibasic acids with diamines to form other types of polyamide resins. J. W. Hill collaborated on much of the early studies. It was shown by Carothers that the key to forming linear polymers lies in the use of materials which are bifunctional, in the sense that a given molecule has two and only two reactive groups. In the case of the polyamides, the functional groups are amino groups and carboxyl groups, which may be distributed so that the molecule contains one amino and one carboxyl group, or that, of two molecules, one would contain two amino groups and the other two carboxyl groups.

In contrast to the polyester resins, which were also studied by Carothers, it was found that the polyamide resins are, in general, high-melting solids which have a high degree of crystallinity. The high melting points were attributed to recurrence of the amide group. The most promising member of the nylon family, nylon-6,6, was first prepared in February, 1935, from adipic acid and hexamethylenediamine.

As a result of exploratory and developmental work on these new products, the Du Pont Company was encouraged in 1939 to set up a plant for the manufacture of nylon products. Since then, plants have been opened by a number of other companies in this country and in Europe, and *nylon* has become a commonplace household word. The term has come to mean a polyamide capable of being drawn into filaments and fibers.

Nylon was first sold in the form of filament bristles and first appeared on the consumer market as bristles on "Dr. West's Miracle Tuft Toothbrushes."

One year later, in 1939, nylon stockings became available for retail sale. During the first year, 64,000,000 pairs of women's nylon stockings were sold.

Nylon molding powders were offered for sale in 1941. Continuing research has brought molding powders to the stage where advanced techniques can be used, and the products are well established where the especially valued properties of nylon are needed.

The polymers of ϵ-caprolactam are sold under the trade name "Perlon L" in Europe and are referred to as nylon-6 in this country. The polyamide resins made from polymerized vegetable oil acids are offered for sale under the trademark "Versamid." The trade-mark "Rilsan" is used for the commercial polyamide resin products made from 11-aminoundecanoic acid and are often called polyamide-11. The properties of these products and of various nylons will be discussed in greater detail in later chapters.

Many of the desirable attributes of polyamides which make them useful for textiles, for filaments, for molding compounds and for surface coatings are well-known. These include high tensile strength, the ability to become oriented on cold-drawing, and the chemical resistance of the amide linkage. Various other characteristics, including molecular weight and distribution of molecular weight, are also important. Chemical modification by other reactions to alter the structure of a given condensation polymer can also be accomplished.

There is great diversity in types of polyamide resins. This is dependent upon choice of starting materials, degree of reaction, later modification through other chemical reactions, and combination or alloying of polyamide resins with other substances. The more common types of polyamide resins available today include nylon-6,6, prepared by the condensation of hexamethylenediamine and adipic acid carried to a molecular weight of approximately 20,000 to 50,000; nylon-6,10, prepared from hexamethylenediamine and sebacic acid and carried to a molecular weight of about the same order; polymers of epsilon-aminocaproic acid made by thermal polymerization of ϵ-aminocaproic acid or caprolactam, and called nylon-6; the self-condensation product of 11-aminoundecanoic acid, or polyamide-11; and polymers prepared from polymerized, unsaturated fatty acids and various polyamino compounds carried to rather low molecular weights of the order of 2,000 to 10,000. The nylon numbering system is an abbreviated description of the materials used in preparation. For example, nylon-6,10 means that the diamine contained 6 carbon atoms and the dibasic acid contained 10 carbon atoms. Nylon-6 is made by polymerization of the 6-carbon, ϵ-aminocaproic acid or caprolactam.

Various systems are used for showing the composition by numbering. In this book, wherever possible, the term *nylon* or *polyamide* will be followed by the number; and word and number will be separated by a hyphen. If there are two or more numbers, they will be separated.

Where there is only one number, it means that the polymer was prepared from a single monomeric substance. The number will be the number of carbon atoms in the linear chain of the recurring polymer units. Polyamides made from amino acids, amino esters and lactams normally will be designated by a single number. Where there are two numbers, two reactants (dibasic acid and diamine, or their equivalents) have been used in forming the polymer. The first number represents the number of carbon atoms in the chain of the diamine, and the second indicates the number of carbon atoms in the dibasic acid chain. In copolymer resins, the major constituents are given first by numbers, and diagonal lines are used to separate the minor constituents. For example, the polyamide resin copolymer -6,6/6,10/6 is a polymer made from a major portion of hexamethylenediamine and adipic acid, and successively smaller portions of hexamethylenediamine and sebacic acid, and finally of ϵ-caprolactam. Percentage composition may be shown in parentheses. Lateral substituents on the linear chains are shown by conventional Greek letter designation. For example, 6,α-Me6 refers to hexamethylenediamine and α-methyladipic acid reactants.

Carothers considered polymerization as a chemical combination involving the operation of primary valence forces and stated that a polymer should not be used to name loose or vaguely defined molecular aggregates. He also defined polymerization as a chemical combination of a number of similar molecules to form a single molecule, thus embracing both condensation polymerization and addition polymerization.

Polymer Type	Intermediates	Remarks
Ester	Hydroxyacid or glycol and dibasic acid	Fiber forming
Amide	Aminoacid or diamine and dibasic acid	Fiber forming
Thioamide	Amine, nitrile, H_2S	—
Urethane	Diisocyanate or dicarbamate and glycol	Fiber forming
Thiourethane	Diisothiocyanate and dithiol	Not fiber forming
Urea	Diisocyanate or urea with diamine	Fiber forming
Thiourea	Diamine and NH_4CNS or trithiocarbonate	Fiber forming
Acetal	Glycol and acetal	Unstable
Thioether	Dithiol and dihalide	Fiber forming
Sulfone	Oxidation of thioether polymer	Fiber forming
Anhydride	Dibasic acid and acetic anhydride	Unstable
Ether	Chlorhydrin and alkali	—
Sulfonamide	Diamine and sulfonic acid or halide	Brittle fibers
Hydrocarbon	Dihalide and sodium	—

By permission of The Society of Dyers and Colourists.

Many types of linear polymers were studied in the exploratory stages of the work by Carothers and associates.* R. J. Hill[1] has summarized some of the pertinent facts about these polymers showing the broad range of materials examined while seeking polymers of the most desirable characteristics.

Although a great many synthetic polyamide resins have been prepared and studied, only a limited number have yet met the test of commercialization. These are polymers made from:

(1) Hexamethylenediamine and adipic acid
(2) ε-caprolactam
(3) Hexamethylenediamine and sebacic acid
(4) Polymerized vegetable oil acids and polyalkylene polyamines
(5) 11-Aminoundecanoic acid
(6) Hexamethylenediamine, ε-caprolactam, adipic acid and sebacic acid (copolymer)
(7) Hexamethylenediamine and adipic acid, modified with formaldehyde and methanol.

These materials provide a range of polymer types varying greatly in properties and utility. They range from liquids to high-melting, crystalline solids and find use as fibers and filaments, films, extrusions, moldings, castings, adhesives, surface coatings, and modifiers.

---

* Much of the original work has been described in the following articles and patents, of which W. H. Carothers is author or co-author:

J. Am. Chem. Soc. **52,** 314 (1930)
J. Am. Chem. Soc. **52,** 711 (1930)
J. Am. Chem. Soc. **52,** 3292 (1930)
J. Am. Chem. Soc. **54,** 1557 (1932)
J. Am. Chem. Soc. **54,** 1559 (1932)
J. Am. Chem. Soc. **54,** 1559 (1932)
J. Am. Chem. Soc. **54,** 1566 (1932)
U.S. patents 1,995,291; 2,012,267; 2,071,250; 2,071,251; 2,071,252; 2,071,253; 2,130,525; 2,130,947; 2,130,948 (assigned to E. I. du Pont de Nemours and Co.)

The high molecular weight superpolymers, capable of being cold-drawn to become oriented, make up the major part of total polyamide resin production. A total production figure and distribution breakdown is not accurately known, but it is estimated that production of polyamide resins for textiles, bristles, other fiber forms, gears and other molded products, adhesives and coatings amounted to about 300,-000,000 pounds in 1955.

Manufacturers of the polyamide resins in this country are E. I. du Pont de Nemours and Company, General Mills, Inc., Barrett Division of Allied Chemical and Dye Corporation, Spencer Chemical Company, Chemstrand Corporation, and American Enka Corporation. There are a number of manufacturers in other countries. It is possible that we may soon see more activity in the field as more and more of the original patents reach their expiration dates.

Commercialization has been dependent not only on the basic chemical studies of polymer formation and on engineering development of methods for making the polymers into fibers and other useful forms, but also on the development of economic manufacturing processes for the intermediates. It was necessary to find suitable methods for the manufacture of adipic acid, hexamethylenediamine, ϵ-caprolactam, sebacic acid and other intermediates. This is deserving of more detailed discussion in later pages.

Polyamide resins are relatively expensive, as resin prices go, largely because of the high costs of the intermediates used in manufacture, in spite of the excellent research on their preparation.

Those based on polymerized vegetable oil acids and polyalkylene polyamines are priced at 50 cents per pound and upward while the nylon types are priced near $1.60 per pound. In spite of high costs and prices, the special and desirable properties possessed by this family of resins has kept them in an important position in the field of resins and plastics and will probably maintain them there in the foreseeable future.

Some of the common trade-marks are:

Name	Description
"Zytel"	A series of Du Pont nylon molding powders from reaction of diamines and dibasic acids
"Rilsan"	Polyamide-11 from 11-aminoundecanoic acid, made by Organico in France
"Tynex"	Filaments of Du Pont nylon from dibasic acids and diamines
"Versamid"	A series of polymers made by General Mills, Inc. from dimerized linoleic acid and polyamines
"Perlon-L"	German version of nylon-6 from ϵ-caprolactam
"Nylenka"	Polycaprolactam polyamide of American Enka Corporation
"Plaskon" nylon	Nylon-6 made by Barrett Division of Allied Chemical and Dye
"Grilon"	A type of nylon-6 made in Switzerland
"Akulon"	Polycaprolactam polymer of Algemene Kunstzijde Unie in Holland

The numbering of grades or types accompanying each trade name has little or nothing to do with the composition numbering system, previously discussed.

Polyamide resins were among the first developed of the linear polymers, are probably the best known, and are among the most important. Full credit must certainly be given to W. H. Carothers and his fellow workers for establishing the basic principles which have made polyamide resins useful.

REFERENCES

1. Hill, R. J., *J. Soc. Dyers Colourists,* **68,** 158 (1952).

2. GENERAL PROPERTIES OF THE POLYAMIDE RESINS

According to W. H. Carothers[6], "the higher the molecular weight, the degree of linear symmetry, the polarity of the unit, and the degree of molecular orientation, the higher will be the melting point, the insolubility, the tensile strength, the flexibility, transparency, elasticity, and luster of the resultant fiber."

The effect of molecular weight on polyester properties can be seen by examination of Table 2.1.

TABLE 2.1. EFFECT OF MOLECULAR WEIGHT ON POLYESTER PROPERTIES

Mol. Wt	M.P., °C	Fiber Forming Ability	Tensile Strength
780	66-7	None	—
3190	68-70	None	—
7330	74	Slight	Weak
16900	77-8	Yes	18600 psi

It is interesting to compare the molecular size of several of the more common types of polymers.

Polymer Material	Mol. Wt	D.P.
Nylon-6,6	16,000-32,000	150-300
Cellophane	5,000-6,000	300-500
Polystyrene for molding	120,000-180,000	1200-1800

Obviously, it is not high molecular weight alone which accounts for the unique and desirable properties of polyamide resins, but rather molecular weight combined with the other factors outlined by Carothers.

Polyamide Classes

Chemically, it is convenient to divide the polyamide resins into the following four classes:

(1) those made by polymerization of lactams;
(2) those made by condensation of a diamine with a dibasic acid, to give a product of high molecular weight;
(3) polyamides made by self-condensation of amino acids;
(4) vegetable oil-based polyamide resins.

There are certain sub groups for each of these types which will be discussed later. In addition, comparisons will be made of polyamides of a given class in which substituent groups are placed along the chains, as for example, C-methyl and N-methyl substituted nylon; and also chemically modified products, such as nylons which have been treated with formaldehyde in the presence of an alcohol to introduce an alkoxy methyl group on the nitrogen atoms. Observations concerning differences between polyamide resins taken to a moderate molecular weight and those taken to a very high molecular weight, in other words between polyamides and the so-called superpolyamides, will be included too.

Caprolactam Polymers

Polyamide resins manufactured by polymerization of lactams are best represented by the most common member of that group, nylon-6, made by polymerization of ε-caprolactam. In the process of polymerizing the lactam, an equilibrium mixture is established consisting of about 90 per cent polymer and 10 per cent unchanged monomer. Part of the unchanged monomer can be removed, which will greatly effect the properties of the final product. The molecular weight of the product will also have a large effect on properties. On a practical basis, to make products of reproducible properties, it has become important for manufacturers to control average chain lengths of the polymer and to control the residual monomer content in the polymer. Average chain length is often controlled by including in the reaction mixture a chain stopper compound such as a low molecular weight aliphatic acid. Acetic acid is often used for this purpose.

Other Nylons

Of the polyamides made by condensation of dibasic acids with diamines, probably the best representatives are the 6,6 and 6,10 types. The 6,6 type, of course, is manufactured from hexamethylenediamine and adipic acid, while the 6,10 type is manufactured from hexamethylenediamine and sebacic acid. Both are normally taken to a very high molecular weight in the order of 15,000. A comparison of nylon-6,6 and nylon-6,10 taken to about the same order of high molecular weight is shown in Table 2.2, along with the properties of nylon-6.

Melting points of various nylon polymers are:[1]

Type	6,6	6,10	10,6	10,10
M.P. °C	265	215	230	196

Perhaps it is more than coincidence that the highest melting polymer is the one of greatest application development.

Table 2.2. Comparison of Properties of Polyamides

Properties	Units	ASTM Method	"Rilsan" BM-D	Nylon-6,6	Nylon-6,10	Nylon-6
Density	—	D792-48T	1.045	1.14	1.09	1.13
Tensile strength: at 73°F	lb/in.^{2}	D638-46T	8,500	10,500	7,000	12,000
at 170°F	lb/in.^{2}	D638-46T	6,800	7,600	6,760	
Elongation: at 73°F	%	D638-46T	120	90	90	300
at 170°F	%	D638-46T	350	320	320	
Modulus of elasticity at 73°F	lb/in.^{2}	D638-46T	178,000	400,000	260,000	300,000
Rockwell hardness	—	D785-48T	R100.5	R118	R111	R118
Flow temperature	°F	D569-48	356	>480	397	419
Coefficient of linear thermal expansion	°F	D696-44	5.5×10^{-5}	5.5×10^{-5}	8.2×10^{-5}	4.6×10^{-5}
Thermal conductivity	BTU/hr/ ft^2/°F/in.	—	1.5	1.7	1.5	1.7
Specific heat	—	—	0.5	0.4	0.4	0.4
Dielectric strength (short time)	Volts/mil	D149-44	430	385	470	420
Volume resistivity	ohm-cm	D257-46	4×10^{14}	4.5×10^{13}	4×10^{14}	4.5×10^{13}
Dielectric constant at 10^3 cycles	—	D150-47T	3.5	4.0	4.5	
Power factor at 10^3 cycles	—	D150-47T	0.03	0.02	0.04	
Water absorption	%	D570-42	0.4	1.5	0.4	1.6
Flammability	in./min	D635-44	self extinguishing	self extinguishing	self extinguishing	—
Chemical effect of:						
Weak acids			None	None		
Strong acids			Attacked by	Attacked by		
Weak alkalis			None	None		
Strong alkalis			None	None		
Alcohols			None	None		
Esters			None	None		
Aliphatic hydrocarbons			None	None		
Aromatic hydrocarbons			None	None		

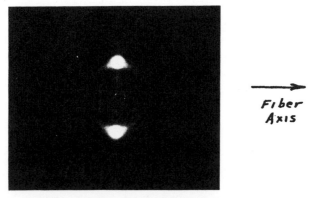

Fiber
Axis

X-ray Diffraction Pattern of Nylon-6,6 (Drawn)
Courtesy Du Pont Co.

The nylon-6,6 (hexamethylenediamine-adipic acid) is readily soluble in phenol, *m*-cresol, xylenols, and formic acid at room temperature and is soluble to the extent of one per cent in crotyl phenol, secondary amyl phenol, ortho-

X-ray Diffraction Pattern of Nylon-6,6 (Undrawn)
Courtesy Du Pont Co.

allylphenol, glycerol mono- and dichlorohydrin, ethylene bromo- and chlorohydrin, acetic acid, lactic acid, thioglycolic acid, 2,3-dibromopropane, and phenylethyl alcohol.[9] It is scarcely affected by most other solvents.

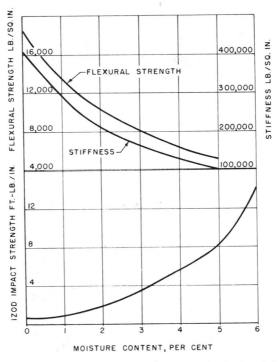

Figure 2.1. Effect of Moisture Content on Nylon-6,6.

As normally produced, nylon-6,6 has a high degree of crystallinity. When quickly cooled or quenched it solidifies in an amorphous form which is much clearer, being nearly translucent. The amorphous form melts lower than the crystalline form.

Increasing moisture content in nylon-6,6 lowers stiffness

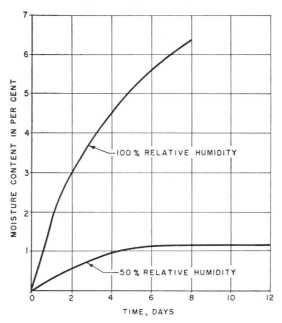

Figure 2.2. Moisture Absorption of Nylon-6,6
at Different Humidities.

and flexural strength, and increases impact strength.[9] This
is shown graphically in Figures 2.1 and 2.2.

Nylon Modification

Substituting a methyl group on the carbon chain in adipic
acid has a profound effect on the properties of the polymer
obtained by condensation with hexamethylenediamine.[10]
This can be seen in Table 2.3.

It is believed that the effect is caused by blocking of
hydrogen bonding by preventing adjacent polymer chains
from packing close together. An even greater effect is noted
if the methyl group is substituted on the nitrogen atom of

hexamethylenediamine. Here a two-fold effect is obtained: the blocking effect just mentioned, plus a reduction of the number of available hydrogen atoms which can take part in hydrogen bonding.

TABLE 2.3. MELTING POINTS OF DIFFERENT POLYAMIDE PRODUCTS

Diamine	Dibasic Acid	M.P., °C
Hexamethylenediamine	Adipic acid	265
Hexamethylenediamine	α-Methyl adipic acid	166
Hexamethylenediamine	β-Methyl adipic acid	216
3-Methyl hexamethylenediamine	Adipic acid	180

Modification of nylon-6,6 by substitution of alkyl groups makes possible changes in properties, to enlarge the scope of uses for polymers of this type[2] (see Figure 2.3). Another

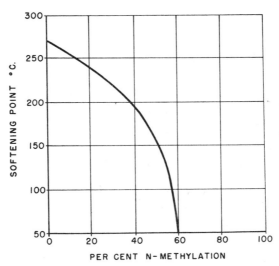

Figure 2.3. Modification of Nylon-6,6 by N-Methyl Substitution. Reprinted from *Industrial and Engineering Chemistry* by permission of the American Chemical Society.

method for changing properties consists of chemical modification by reaction of the amide groups of the nylon with formaldehyde. This is most often done in the presence of an alcohol in order to permit formation of an alkoxy methyl group on the nitrogen atoms. The greater the amount of modification, chemically speaking, the greater will be the effect on physical properties. In general, methoxy methyl substitution on nylon-6,6 lowers the melting point and increases solubility, as can be seen by the data reproduced[5] in Table 2.4.

TABLE 2.4. EFFECT OF N-ALKOXY METHYL SUBSTITUTION
IN NYLON-6,6*

% Substitution	% Solubility in 80% Ethanol	M.P., °C	% Elastic Stretch
0	0	265	45
22	25	185	285
32	50	130	375

* Reprinted from *Journal of the American Chemical Society* by permission of the American Chemical Society.

These same methods of modification can also be applied to other nylons, as for example, nylon-6,10. Therefore, a wide range of products of varying solubilities, melting points and other properties can be obtained with a relatively small number of starting materials. Of course, the much larger range of products extends the potential uses for this family of resins.

Physical and Chemical Effects

Certain chemicals and solvents exert a noticeable effect on the properties of polyamides, as exemplified[9] in Table 2.5

TABLE 2.5. EFFECT OF CHEMICALS ON NYLONS

Chemical	Nylon-6.6						Nylon-6.10					
	1 Week			1 Month			1 Week			1 Month		
	Wt % Gain	Dimens. Change in/in	Tensile Strength	Wt % Gain	Dimens. Change in/in	Tensile Strength	Wt % Gain	Dimens. Change in/in	Tensile Str'gth	Wt % Gain	Dimens. Change in/in	Tensile Strength
Sulfuric acid, 30%	2.4	0.0011	8500	4.9	0.0087	4600	1.0	0.0028	8900	1.8	0.0028	8200
Sulfuric acid, 3%	4.2	0.0022	8800	7.0	0.0065	4300	1.0	0.0017	8100	2.0	0.0008	8300
Sodium hydroxide, 1%	2.4	0.0014	8800	4.9	0.0091	9000	0.9	0.0009	4800	1.8	0.0039	8400
Sodium hydroxide, 10%	1.6	0.0013	4400	3.1	0.0039	8100	0.8	0.0010	8800	1.5	0.0013	9000
Ethanol, 50%	3.3	0.0020	8500	7.1	0.015	7600	3.3	0.0027	8600	6.2	0.0120	7700
Ethanol, 95%	1.8	0.0006	9400	3.4	0.0006	8000	4.4	0.0027	8100	3.8	0.0158	8000
Sodium chloride, 10%	0.4	0.0014	9200	3.7	0.0022	10000	0.8	0.0013	9000	1.6	0.0021	8100
Ethyl acetate	<0.1	0.00003	10700	0.1	0.0004	10100	0.1	0.0001	8000	0.3	0.0004	8400
Carbon tetrachloride	0.2	0.0008	10700	0.6	0.0008	9750	0.2	0.0011	7900	0.6	0.0008	8400
Toluene	0.2	0.0008	10100	0.6	0.0008	10000	0.3	0.0006	8200	0.7	0.0008	8400
Heptane	1.9	0.0013	10800	0.6	0.0014	10100	0.2	0.0004	8600	0.5	0.0014	9000
Acetone	<0.1	0.0004	10400	0.1	0.002	10400	0.3	0	8900	0.7	0.0019	8200

concerning nylons-6,6 and -6,10. Although very resistant, long contact with certain reagents brings about gradual changes.

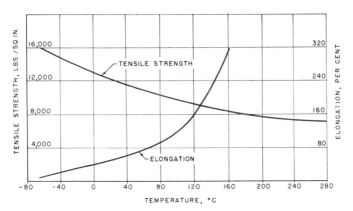

Figure 2.4. Effect of Temperature on Nylon-6,6.

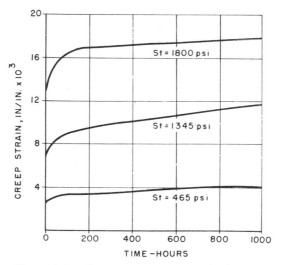

Figure 2.5. Effect of Temperature on Nylon-6,6.

TABLE 2.6. CRITICAL PROPERTIES OF PLASTICS

	Sp. Gr.	Tensile Strength psi $\times 10^3$	Izod Impact at 25°C	Stiffness psi $\times 10^3$	Water Absorption %	Elongation, %	Maximum Service Temp., °C
Acrylic	1.2	7.0	0.4	360	0.275	1.5	100
Cellulose acetate butyrate	1.1	5.0	3.3		1.5	50	75
Hard rubber	1.2	7.5			0.75	3	60
Neoprene	1.35	3.25				590	
"Kel-F"	2.1	6.0	3.5		0	35	200
Polyethylene	0.9	1.8		20	0.1	200	70
Polystyrene	1.0	7.0	0.2	340	0.3	2	80
Polyethylene terephthalate	1.38	17–25			0.3	100	
Rigid polyvinyl chloride	1.35	8.5	0.5	440	0.5	150	70
Saran	1.75	5.0	1.9	50	0.45		80
"Teflon"	2.3	2.0	4.5	50	0	0.2	285
Nylon-6,6	1.1	11.0	1.4	290	1.5	105	130
						45	

Reprinted by permission of the authors and publishers from *Chemical Engineering,* July 1953, Copyright 1953 by McGraw-Hill Publishing Co., New York.

Since they are thermoplastic resins, the polyamide resins are affected by temperature changes. The effects of temperature on certain properties of nylon-6,6 are illustrated in Figures 2.4 and 2.5.

All thermoplastic materials are subject to deformation under load and polyamides are no exception, although they are more resistant than many other materials. Bruner and Wayne[4] have reported the creep characteristics of a number of thermoplastic materials, including nylon-6,6; a curve of creep characteristics of nylon-6,6 under conditions of stress is given in Figure 2.6. They have also shown some of the critical physical properties for 6,6-nylon and other plastics (see Table 2.6).

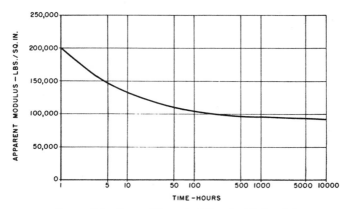

Figure 2.6. Creep Characteristics for Nylon-6,6.
Reprinted by permission of the authors and publisher from *Chemical Engineering*, July 1953, copyright 1953 by McGraw-Hill Publishing Co., New York.

Copolymers

Copolymer resins, prepared from the reaction of two or more diamines with one or more dibasic acids or from one or more diamines with two or more dibasic acids or from the reaction of an amino acid or lactam with a diamine, dibasic acid mixture, differ in many respects from the homopolymers.[1,7] Ordinarily they are lower-melting, more soluble, softer, less stiff, and have lower tensile strengths. The irregularity introduced into the copolymer interferes with intermolecular forces, chiefly hydrogen bonding, between polymer molecules. Also, there is less tendency to crystallinity, since regular spacing between amide groups is disrupted. Normally the effects are related to the mole fractions of respective homopolymer types. This may be seen in Figures 2.7 and 2.8.

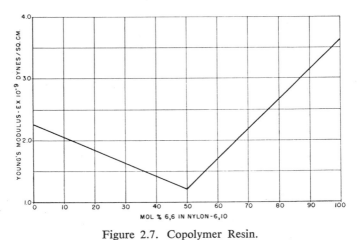

Figure 2.7. Copolymer Resin.
Reprinted from the *Journal of the American Chemical Society* by permission of the American Chemical Society.

Flory and co-workers[8] have shown that polyamides and polyesters show similar copolymer effects and that the degree of change is roughly proportional to the mole fraction of constituents. For example, melting point minima, solubility maxima, and water absorption maxima have been indicated. Flexible multiple interpolymers have been described by Bru-

"Versamids"

Polyamide resins based on polymerized vegetable oil acids are available in several grades, ranging from materials which are liquid at room temperature to hard solid materials melting at temperatures as high as 185°C. These types may be considered internally plasticized by the long carbon chains and the large alkyl substituents on the chains of the dibasic acid portion. "Versamids" are classed as relatively low-melting, highly soluble polyamide resins of low to moderate molecular weight.

Typical properties of the "Versamid" polyamide resins, condensation products of polymerized vegetable oil acids and polyalkylene polyamines, are given in Table 2.8.

The solid series "Versamids" are used "as is," or modified with plasticizers, waxes, and other resins in hot melt cements, heat-seal coatings, barrier coatings, inks and specialty adhesives and coatings. The semisolid and fluid series "Versamid" polyamide resins may be used to modify the solid "Versamids" or may be converted to thermoset resins by reaction with epoxy resins, heat-reactive phenolic resins, and other substances.

Many other types of polyamide resins can be obtained by the use of the various dibasic acids and diamines. There have been recent reports on the use of oxalic acid, isophthalic acid and terephthalic acid in making nylons. In addition, a large number of amines have been mentioned, including those having one primary and one secondary amino group and the disecondary diamines. However, since detailed reports cannot be given for all these products, for the purpose of this chapter, comparisons are made only of those of commercial significance or those which are representative of a class of polyamide resins.

TABLE 2.8. TYPICAL PROPERTIES OF "VERSAMID" POLYAMIDES

	Solid Series			Semisolid Series		Fluid Series	
	900	930	940	950	100	115	125
Amine value	3	3	3	3	3	210-230	290-320
Color-gardner	NDT 12	NDT 12	NDT 12	NDT 12	NDT 12	NDT 12	NDT 12
M.P., °C	180-190	105-115	105-115	95-105	43-53	Fluid	Fluid
Viscosity-poises-40°C	—	—	—	—	—	500-750	80-120
Viscosity-poises-150°C	—	30-45	15-30	7-15	10-15	—	—
% Ash	0.05	0.05	0.05	0.05	0.05	0.05	0.05
Sp. gr.	0.98	0.98	0.98	0.98	0.98	0.99	0.97
Lbs./gallon	8.2	8.2	8.2	8.2	8.2	8.3	8.1
Penetration-25°C-ASTM D5-52	2	3	4	15	100	—	—

Applications versus Properties

It is interesting to review some of the applications for which polyamide resins are used and list the different types which have been found suitable for individual application. It is clear from Table 2.9 that certain types of materials are best fitted for certain applications. The reasons for this are probably more apparent from a study of the physical and chemical properties of the resins themselves than from simple identification by name of type.

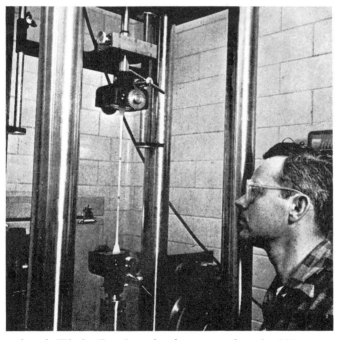

Sample of "Plaskon" nylon showing approximately 300 per cent elongation with a constant pull of more than 12,000 psi.
Courtesy Barrett Division, Allied Chemical and Dye.

TABLE 2.9. END USES FOR POLYAMIDES

Application	Nylon-6.6	Nylon-6.10	Nylon-6	Nylon Copolymers	"Versamids"	"Rilsan" Polymers
Textile fibers	Yes	Some	Yes	Slight	No	Some
Filaments and bristles	Yes	Yes	Yes	Slight	No	Yes
Extrusions	Yes	Yes	Yes	Yes	No	Yes
Moldings	Yes	Yes	Yes	Yes	No	Yes
Film	Slight	Slight	Slight	No	No	Yes
Adhesives	No	No	No	Slight	Yes	?
Thermoplastic cements	No	No	No	No	Yes	Slight
Barrier coatings	No	No	No	Some	Yes	Slight
Thermoset adhesives	No	No	No	No	Yes	No
Thermoset coatings	No	No	No	No	Yes	No
Castings and pottings	No	No	No	No	Yes	No
Sealants	No	No	No	No	Yes	No

For example, it appears that to obtain fiber-forming polyamide resins capable of being drawn into thin filaments of high strength, it is important to have high molecular weight, together with a tendency to become oriented on cold drawing. This is closely related to the resin's potentialities for hydrogen bonding, which enables the fibers to lie parallel to each other, with strong attractive forces between adjacent polymer molecules. As a result, the length of the fiber or polymer molecule is extended and the fibers are closely associated in a tight, strong bundle. Hydrogen bonding also is thought to cross-link the fiber molecules. Orientation by cold drawing will be discussed in the chapter on fibers. It is also important for the polymer molecules to have relatively high melting points so that a fabric made from such fibers does not melt when ironed.

At the other extreme, materials used most successfully in conventional coatings or paints are those which can be applied as liquids or can be readily dissolved to form liquid solutions. This is because paints are normally applied as liquid materials which harden into films on exposure. Other polyamide coatings are possible, but these are the extruded and cast types, and not the conventional wet film coatings.

Polyamide resins used in adhesives are of the coating type, that is, those which can be melted and applied or those which may be dissolved and applied as adhesives—or they are materials which are thermoplastic in nature but converted to thermoset substances by reaction with another material. In any case, it is important again to have material which is inherently liquid or which can be made liquid by mild heating or by dissolving it in a suitable solvent.

In the field of moldings and extrusions, polyamide resins of moderate to high molecular weight are needed. Moderately high melting point is also desirable. The reason is that, for practical work, a resin with too high melting point is difficult and expensive to handle. However, it can also be seen that it is necessary that these moldings and extrusions have a high degree of tensile and structural strength. For this reason, fairly high molecular weight materials are generally chosen.

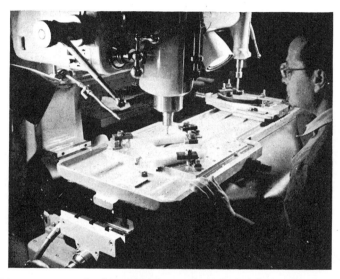

Using a pantograph, this technician at the Polychemicals Sales Service Laboratory of Du Pont is duplicating the profile of an intricate part in a bar of "Zytel" nylon resin. Tests are made on such machined parts before injection molds are built. The new Du Pont laboratory is at Chestnut Run, just outside of Wilmington, Delaware.
Courtesy Du Pont Co.

Polyamide resins are also available in water-dispersed forms. See Chapter 9.

It appears that there is no general-purpose polyamide which is suitable for all known uses. New forms are being introduced to implement the present uses and to expand the field of uses. However, the strong and well-established applications for which polyamide resins have made themselves best known are textile fibers, bristles, molded gears and related mechanical parts, heat-sealing adhesives and co-reactants with epoxy resins for surface coatings and adhesives. Trends in these and other directions and possibilities for future development along other lines will be discussed in a later chapter.

REFERENCES

1. Baker, W. O. and Fuller, C. S., *J. Am. Chem. Soc.*, **64,** 2399 (1942).
2. Biggs, B. S., Frosch, C. J., and Erickson, R. H., *Ind. Eng. Chem.*, **38,** 1016 (1946).
3. Brubaker, M. M. and Wiley, R. H. (to Du Pont), U.S. Patent 2,285,009.
4. Bruner, W. M., and Wayne, P. J., *Chem. Eng.*, **60** (7), 193 (1953).
5. Cairns, J. L., Foster, H. D., Larsher, A. W., Schneider, A. K., and Schreiger, R. S., *J. Am. Chem. Soc.*, **71,** 651 (1949).
6. Carothers, W. H. (to Du Pont), U.S. Patents 2,252,554 and 2,071,250.
7. Catlin, W. E., Czerwin, E. P., and Wiley, R. H., *J. Polymer Sci.*, **2,** 412 (1947).
8. Evans, R. D., Mighton, H. R., and Flory, P. J., *J. Am. Chem. Soc.*, **72,** 2018 (1950).
9. General Zytel Booklet, Du Pont Company (1954).
10. Hill, R. J., *J. Soc. Dyers Colourists*, **68,** 158 (1952).
11. Lewis, J. R. and Reynolds, R. J. W., *Chem. and Ind.*, **45,** 958 (1951).

3. BASIC CHEMISTRY OF THE POLYAMIDES

Raw Materials

The starting materials for making polyamide resins include a number of interesting chemicals. Hexamethylenediamine and adipic acid are two of the most common ones, and both may be derived from phenol.

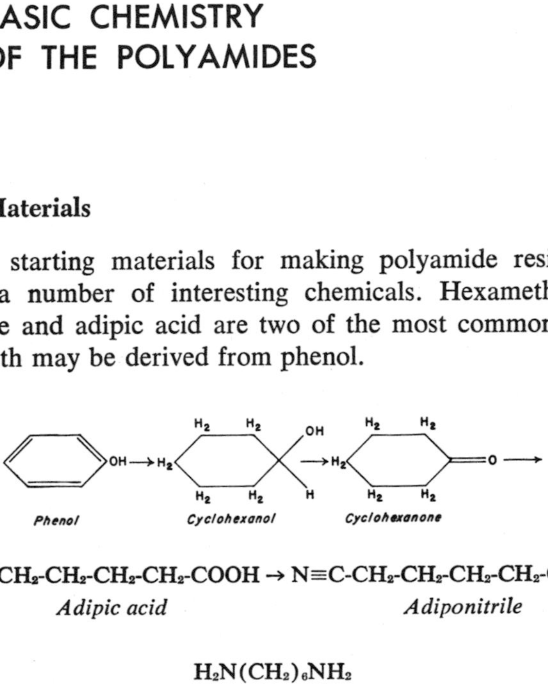

Phenol → Cyclohexanol → Cyclohexanone →

$$HOOC\text{-}CH_2\text{-}CH_2\text{-}CH_2\text{-}CH_2\text{-}COOH \rightarrow N\equiv C\text{-}CH_2\text{-}CH_2\text{-}CH_2\text{-}CH_2\text{-}C\equiv N \rightarrow$$

Adipic acid   *Adiponitrile*

$$H_2N(CH_2)_6NH_2$$

Hexamethylenediamine

Adipic acid can also be prepared by oxidation of cyclohexane with air or nitric acid. The purified acid is obtained in the form of white, monoclinic crystals, melting at 152°C. It is quite soluble in hot water but only slightly soluble in cold water. An alternative method for making hexamethylenediamine is:

$$H_2C-CH_2$$
$$H_2C \quad CH_2 + 2HCl \rightarrow Cl(CH_2)_4Cl + H_2O$$
$$O$$

Tetrahydrofuran   *1,4-Dichlorobutane*

$$Cl(CH_2)_4Cl + 2NaCN \rightarrow NC(CH_2)_4CN + 2NaCl$$
Adiponitrile

$$NC(CH_2)_4CN + 4H_2 \rightarrow H_2N(CH_2)_6NH_2$$
Hexamethylenediamine

In recent years other methods have been worked out and the scope is well illustrated by the flow chart in Figure 3.1.

Sebacic acid is ordinarily manufactured by alkaline cleavage of castor oil acids (ricinoleic acid):

$$OH$$
$$CH_3(CH_2)_5CH\text{-}CH_2CH = CH\text{-}(CH_2)_7COOH \rightarrow$$
Ricinoleic acid

$$OH$$
$$HOOC(CH_2)_8COOH + CH_3(CH_2)_5CHCH_3$$
Sebacic acid   *Octanol-2*

Dilinoleic acid (polymerized vegetable oil acids) may be prepared by the thermal polymerization of linoleic acid.[3] Although the course of the polymerization has not yet been definitely proved, it is believed, according to the bulk of available evidence, to proceed as follows. Part of the natural 9,12-linoleic acid becomes conjugated under the influence

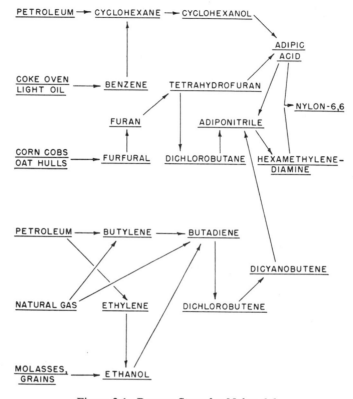

Figure 3.1. Process Steps for Nylon-6,6.
Reprinted from *Industrial and Engineering Chemistry* by permission of the American Chemical Society.

of heat to the 9,11- and 10,12-linoleic acids. These conjugated structures may react with unconjugated 9,12-linoleic acid by a Diels-Alder mechanism to give a dimer. Higher polymers are also formed in lesser quantity. Numerous isomeric forms of the dimer are possible.

Commercial production of ethylenediamine and higher alkylene polyamines is usually brought about by the reaction of ethylene chloride and ammonia:

$$ClCH_2\text{-}CH_2Cl + 4NH_3 \rightarrow H_2NCH_2\text{-}CH_2NH_2 \text{ (and higher alkylene polyamines)} + 2NH_4Cl$$

Other routes include reaction of formaldehyde with HCN and ammonia.

ϵ-Caprolactam and ϵ-aminocaproic acid are derived from phenol by several steps, including hydrogenation to cyclohexanol, oxidation to cyclohexanone, formation of the oxime, and rearrangement to the lactam.

Another method of making the lactam is by reduction of nitrocyclohexane at high temperature.[9]

Amide Formation

Two of the three principal types of polyamide resins depend upon the same reaction for their preparation. These are the types made by self-condensation of amino acids and by reaction of diamines with dicarboxylic acids. The reaction involved is one of amide formation from interaction of a carboxyl group with an amino group with elimination of water. In the reaction of diamino compounds with dicarboxylic acids, there is frequently a preliminary step of salt formation, often conducted in aqueous solution. This is done to adjust equivalent amounts of acid and amine to avoid terminating the polymer chain as a result of an excess of either reagent. The salt is dehydrated by heating to form the amide.

Although catalysts are not ordinarily required for the reaction, occasionally acid compounds are used to hasten the formation of the amide bond. Esters may be used in place of acids, resulting in the formation of by-product alcohols, and producing polymer without use of catalyst.

It has been shown that condensation of certain diamines, such as hexamethylenediamine, with a dibasic acid, such as adipic acid, may be carried out in xylenols at 230°C for six hours in an atmosphere of nitrogen. The water formed is carried away by a rapid current of nitrogen; a vacuum may be needed to bring about condensation to a high polymer stage.

The other main type of polyamide resin, that derived from lactams, such as epsilon-amino caprolactam, is prepared by the thermal polymerization of the lactam itself. Heat alone is sufficient to bring about the polymer formation through an addition reaction. An equilibrium mixture is produced in which monomeric lactam is present to the extent of about 10 per cent—the remaining 90 per cent being polymers of various chain lengths. Chemicals to control chain length are often added. Presumably, polymer formation results from initial hydrolysis of a molecule of the lactam to give epsilon-aminocaproic acid, followed by addition of the lactam to the end groups of this compound, forming a linear chain of increasing length. In place of hydrolyzing a portion of the lactam to start the reaction, it is possible to build the molecules from an added amino acid or from a nylon salt.

$$\underset{\epsilon\text{-}Caprolactam}{\overset{\displaystyle \overline{}CO}{(CH_2)_5\text{-}NH}} + H_2O \rightarrow \underset{\epsilon\text{-}Aminocaproic\ acid}{H_2N(CH_2)_5COOH}$$

$$H_2N(CH_2)_5COOH + \underset{NH}{\overset{CO}{(CH_2)_5}} \rightarrow H_2N(CH_2)_5CONH(CH_2)_5COOH$$

This step is repeated to give a polymer:

$$H\left[HN(CH_2)_5CO\right]_n OH$$

Polymer

$$\text{Average molecular weight} = \frac{2 \times 10^6}{C(NH_2) + C(COOH)}$$

C = concentration in equiv./million grams polymer.

Normally, if the combination of diamine and dibasic acid or the amino acid is capable of forming a five or six member ring, ring formation will be favored over polymer formation. With amino acids of the general formula $H_2N(CH_2)xCOOH$, polymer formation is favored if x is equal to or greater than 5.

Other Methods for Polyamides

There are other known methods for forming amide groups and a few of these have been explored as routes to polyamide formation. However, they have not yet assumed commercial significance. Among the methods should be mentioned the reaction of nitriles with olefins and with tertiary alcohols.[13] Reaction of dinitriles with ditertiary glycols or their esters is illustrated below.

$$NC\text{-}R'\text{-}CN + HO\overset{|}{C}\text{-}R_2\text{-}\overset{|}{C}\text{-}OH \xrightarrow{\text{Strong acid}} NC\text{-}R'\text{-}CONH\overset{|}{C}\text{-}R_2\text{-}\overset{|}{C}OH$$

R′ = alkylene radical
R₂ = alkylene radical

This unit can react with either or both of the starting materials, increasing in molecular weight with each step.

Ditertiary olefins and halides also undergo essentially the same reaction as the ditertiary glycols, in the presence of a strong acid. This has even led to self-polymerization of the β-unsaturated nitrile, acrylonitrile.

Formaldehyde has been shown to react with dinitriles in the presence of strong acids:[14]

$$NC\text{-}R\text{-}CN + H_2CO \rightarrow NC\text{-}R\text{-}\left[CO\text{-}NH\text{-}CH_2\text{-}NH\text{-}CO\text{-}R\text{-}\right]_n CN$$

Dinitrile   *Polymer*

Stability of Polyamides

Polyamide resins are not perfectly stable to ultraviolet light, especially in the presence of air. There is a tendency to lose tensile strength and to discolor. This may result from oxidation of amino groups and amide groups of the polymer molecule due to the effect of radiant energy on the polymer in the presence of oxygen. Antioxidants of various kinds are effective in stabilizing the resins against the effects of oxygen and ultraviolet light. Some of these include mercaptobenzothiazole, syringic acid and various phenolic antioxidants, chromium salts and copper salts.

When nylon-6,6 is heated in air it gradually oxidizes. The oxidation is accompanied by a decrease in molecular weight and the product turns brown. When heated in the absence of air nylon-6,6 slowly forms a gel, brought about by decomposition in the adipic acid portion of the molecule. Various by-products, including carbon dioxide, ammonia, and cyclopentanone, result from this decomposition.[17]

Cross-linked polymers are formed by heating the linear nylon polymers at 260°C in the presence of traces of oxygen. These cross-linked polymers can be softened but do not melt and, although they swell in hot phenols, they do not dissolve nor can they be drawn into filaments. They can be converted to the linear soluble polymers if heated at 100°C for five hours in hydrochloric acid.

Occasionally it is desirable to deluster resins, particularly resin fibers. This is accomplished by incorporation of a small amount of titanium oxide, zinc oxide, carbon black, barium sulfate, or other suitable pigment. However, pigment augments loss of strength in the presence of ultraviolet light and, therefore, it is more necessary to use stabilizing agents.

The polymers are stable when heated with water or water and a phenol at 170°C, but a little hydrolysis occurs when the temperature is raised to about 200°C. This reaction may be useful for recovering scrap polyamides. With hydrochloric acid, some hydrolysis occurs at 100°C in six hours.

Orientation and Intermolecular Forces

There is a great tendency for polyamide resins to become oriented through intermolecular, secondary valence forces. The carbonyl group of the amide linkage of a polyamide unit can become associated with the hydrogen attached to the amino group of the amide linkage of an adjacent molecule. If the distances between amide groups in adjacent molecule chains are such that hydrogen bonding is facilitated as in nylon-6,6, strong intermolecular forces can be formed. The intermolecular forces have a great effect on melting point, fiber tensile strength, solubility and general usefulness of the polymers. If carried to sufficiently high molecular weights— for example, 10,000 or greater—polyamides are capable of being cold-drawn or stretched at moderately low temperatures; this facilitates orientation and increases tensile strength considerably. Where the carbon chains in the polymers have odd numbers of atoms, there is less intermolecular bonding, and lower melting points are observed. Intermolecular bonding also leads to greater crystallinity and lower solubility.

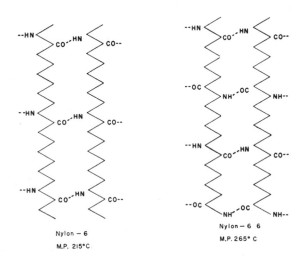

Nylon — 6
M.P. 215°C

Nylon — 6 6
M.P. 265° C

The melting points of some of the nylons prepared by Carothers are shown in Table 3.1.

Polyamide resins differ from many other polymer types which show much weaker hydrogen bonding.

Generally speaking, the polyester resins are softer, lower melting, and less strong than polyamides made from the same dibasic acid. This difference is largely due to a lower degree of intermolecular bonding between polymer chains, since there is less tendency toward hydrogen bonding in the polyester resins, many of which are actually liquids. An exception is the polymer of ethylene glycol and terephthalic acid, which has a high melting point and excellent strength.

Polyester amides, derived from dibasic acids, and amino alcohols, have properties intermediate between polyamides

TABLE 3.1. APPROXIMATE MELTING POINTS (IN AIR)*
FOR VARIOUS NYLONS

Diamine	Dibasic Acid	M.P., °C, of Nylon
Ethylene	Sebacic	254
Tetramethylene	Adipic	278
Tetramethylene	Suberic	250
Tetramethylene	Azelaic	223
Tetramethylene	Sebacic	239
Pentamethylene	Glutaric	198
Pentamethylene	Adipic	223
Pentamethylene	Pimelic	183
Pentamethylene	Suberic	202
Pentamethylene	Azelaic	178
Hexamethylene	Sebacic	209
Octamethylene	Adipic	235
Octamethylene	Sebacic	197
Decamethylene	Carbonic	200
Decamethylene	Oxalic	229
Decamethylene	Sebacic	194
p-Xylylene	Sebacic	268
Piperazine	Sebacic	153

* Melting points are higher in absence of air.

and polyesters.[5] It is certainly true that one very notable
feature of the polyamide resins is the strong intermolecular
bonding between adjacent molecules.

Polyamide Interaction

Blends of two different polyamides will co-react when
heated above the melting point, first to give block copolymers, followed by segment interchange gradually leading to
random copolymers.[1] For example, a blend of nylons-6,6

and 6,10 when heated long enough (in the absence of air) at high temperature forms the random 6,6/6,10 copolymer. The same copolymer may be arrived at more quickly and directly through the reaction of adipic and sebacic acids, together with hexamethylenediamine.

Copolymer Resins

It is generally true that the copolymer resins are lower melting and more soluble than the homopolymers which can be made from the same ingredients. This is because the degree of crystallinity is reduced and also because the regularity of appearance of amide groups in a copolymer is disturbed, thus reducing the likelihood of hydrogen bond formation between adjacent chains.[15] If the disorder is not great the copolymer will have properties intermediate between the possible homopolymers.

Modification of Polyamides

Various methods are known for modification of the polyamide resins. Most of the modification results from chemical reaction with the amide groups. Cairns[4] has shown that reaction of a polyamide with formaldehyde in the presence of an alcohol brings about substitution of methoxymethyl groups on the amide nitrogens. This lowers the melting point of the polymer and increases its solubility. If carried far enough, it can even produce materials with rubber-like properties.

Polyamide resins may also be modified by substituting groups of different kinds in the molecule chain. For example, substitution of an alkyl group on the carbon chain lowers melting point and increases solubility. Substitution of an alkyl group on a nitrogen atom has an even greater effect.[12]

A polyamide from hexamethylenediamine and adipic acid

melts at 265°C. If α-methyl adipic acid is used, the melting point of the polymer is 166°C, and with β-methyl adipic acid the melting point is 216°C. The polymer from 3-methyl hexamethylenediamine and adipic acid melts at 180°C. The greatest effect of methyl substitution is shown with N-methyl hexamethylenediamine where reaction with adipic acid gives a polyamide with melting point lowered to 145°C.

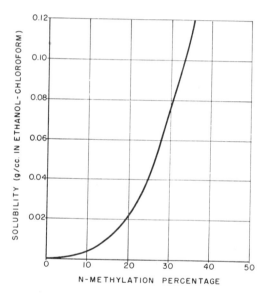

Figure 3.2. Effect of N-Methylation on Solubility of Nylon-6,6. Reprinted from the *Journal of the American Chemical Society* by permission of the American Chemical Society.

Substitution of alkyl groups on the carbon chains serves to block the polymer molecule away from adjacent molecules, reducing the hydrogen bonding between adjacent chains. Substituents on the nitrogen atom also exert this blocking effect and tend to increase it by reducing the number of hydrogen atoms available for bonding.

The effect of degree of N-methylation in polydecameth-
ylene sebacamides on solubility and on rigidity has been
reported graphically by Baker and Fuller.[2] See Figures 3.2
and 3.3.

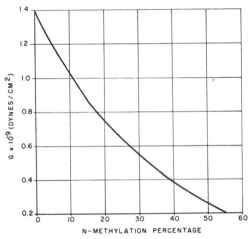

Figure 3.3. Effect of N-Methylation on Young's Modulus
with Nylon-6,6.
Reprinted from the *Journal of the American Chemical Society* by
permission of the American Chemical Society.

It has also been observed that insertion of hetero atoms,
such as oxygen or sulfur, in place of one of the carbon
atoms of either the dibasic acid or diamine brings about
irregularity and permits greater freedom of movement, resulting in lower melting point and greater solubility.

Molecular Weight

Polyamide molecules differ considerably in molecular
weight and chain length. A given reaction mixture will con-

tain molecules of widely varying size, covering a wide molecular weight range. This is because the reaction is a random affair, which does not complete polyamide formation, for 100 per cent reaction would produce a single molecule of infinite molecular weight.

Control of molecular weight has been accomplished by various means. Some workers have used an excess of either of the two common reagents. Others have controlled polymerization by using a slight amount of an end group terminator, such as acetic acid.

When the term molecular weight is used in reference to polyamide resins, what is actually meant is average molecular weight of all the molecules. At least two types of averages may be determined. There are the number average molecular weight, *Mn*, which equals $1/\Sigma \dfrac{fi}{Mi}$ and the weight average molecular weight, *Mw*, which equals $\Sigma\ fi\ mi$, where fi is the fractional weight of constituent of molecular weight *Mi* in the polymer mixture.

Mn is ordinarily determined by end group titration methods or osmotic methods while *Mw* may be obtained by viscosity measurements. As Carothers[6] has pointed out, *Mn* and *Mw* will be equal where the polymer chains are of identical size, but will differ when, as in most polymer products, there is distribution of molecular weights. For example, if there is a mixture of 10 molecules of weight 100 and of weight 1000, *Mn* is 400, but *Mw* is 851.

Mz, the sedimentation average molecular weight, is very useful with polymers of very large size.[16]

Typical distribution curves for polymer molecules of different sizes (found in polyamide resins and other condensation polymer mixtures), adapted from Flory[10], are shown in Figure 3.4. Here "*n*" or degree of polymerization (number of condensation units) is plotted against the weight fraction of molecules having a given number of such units, at different extents of reaction, represented by *p*. For example, at $p = 0.90$, the reaction is 90 per cent complete and at $p = 0.99$ it is 99 per cent complete.

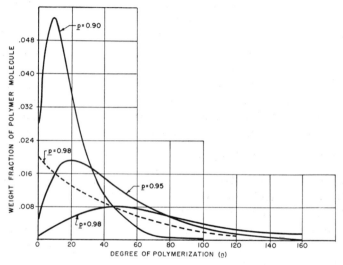

Figure 3.4. Molecular Weight Distribution in Nylon at Various Degrees of Polymerization.
Reprinted from the *Journal of the American Chemical Society* by permission of the American Chemical Society.

When *n* is plotted against mole fraction (instead of weight fraction) of molecules having a given number of units, a different curve is obtained, which shows that at any stage of reaction, monomer molecules predominate over other unit species. On the weight basis this is not the case.

Molecular weights of polyamide resins may range from those having essentially dimer formation to those having a degree of polymerization in excess of 100. Carothers was first to use the term super-polymers or super-polyamides for those condensation products he prepared in which the polymers had an average molecular weight of 10,000 or more. To reach this value Carothers changed from a simple reaction vessel to a molecular still for the latter stages of the reaction.[7] This made it possible to eliminate the by-product of the reaction (water or other matter having little tendency to distill out of a reaction vessel), thus forcing the reaction to proceed further in the direction of polymer formation.

The super-polymers or super-polyamides have noticeably different characteristics from those of the low molecular weight products. They tend to have higher melting points, greater ability to form strong fibers, and greater tendency towards crystallinity, as determined by x-ray study.

Molecular weight of 10,000 or greater and ability to form intermolecular secondary bonds are requirements for making polyamide resins capable of forming strong fibers and capable of being cold drawn. The term "nylon" was coined to define such polyamide resins. The relationship between molecular weight and degree of polymerization for nylon-6,6 is shown in Table 3.2.

TABLE 3.2. NYLON-6,6

Reaction %	Chemical Change	D.P.	Approx. M. Wt.
50	1 COOH of each molecule reacted 1 NH_2	= 2	250
75	0.75 x 2 mole H_2O produced	= 4	500
90	0.9 x 2 mole H_2O produced	= 10	1250
95	0.95 x 2 mole H_2O produced	= 20	2500
99.17	0.9917 x 2 mole H_2O produced	=120	15000

Reactive Polyamides

Polyamide resins containing reactive carboxyl or amino groups may be prepared by using an excess of either the amino reagent or the carboxylic acid reagent.[11] Normally, this will lead to low molecular weight, providing difunctional acid and difunctional amine are used. However, if one of the reagents is difunctional and the other trifunctional, and if they are reacted in appropriate proportion, high molecular weight substances containing either a free carboxyl or free amino group may be formed. For example, if dimeric fatty acids, such as dilinoleic acid, are reacted with diethylene triamine[8] on a mole to mole basis, one free amino group will remain for every unit in the polymer chain. Care must be exercised to prevent gelation in preparation of such polymers. A polymer of this kind has an equivalent weight as an amino compound which is approximately the value of the unit weight of each unit of the polymer, in this instance, about 600. The amino group may be titrated by dissolving the reaction product in a suitable solvent, such as isopropyl alcohol, and titrating with dilute aqueous acid. In this way, the amine number may be determined. Reaction of the carboxyl group with the amino group in this instance takes place preferentially at the primary amino group although it is known that the secondary amino group is also involved to some extent.

Dimer acid   *Diethylene triamine*

Acid number = milligrams of KOH which correspond to 1 gram of the acid.

Amine number = milligrams of KOH which correspond to 1 gram of the amine.

For both determinations the polymer product is dissolved in butanol or a higher alcohol. The solution is titrated against a suitable indicator with dilute, standard aqueous sodium hydroxide solution for the acid number determination and with dilute, standard aqueous hydrochloric acid for the amine number determinations.

Resin Alloys

Amino-containing polyamide resins are capable of reaction with a number of materials. Their interaction with epoxy compounds has been the basis for the development of a group of new resin alloys or thermoset reaction products of epoxy resins and epoxy compounds with the amino-containing polyamide resins.[11] These products undergo a reaction or cure as illustrated below. In addition, the two resins modify each other's properties as do alloy metals. The epoxy resin imparts strength, wettability, a low degree of shrinkage and the ability to cure at relatively low temperature while the polyamide portion of the molecule confers toughness, adhesion, resiliency and wetting action. The combination, unlike either resin alone, has new properties and is thermosetting. Neither of the two resins may be recovered from the reaction mixture.

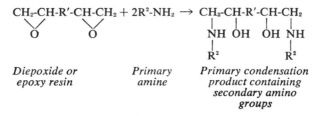

| *Diepoxide or epoxy resin* | *Primary amine* | *Primary condensation product containing secondary amino groups* |

$$CH_2\text{-}CH\text{-}R'\text{-}CH\text{-}CH_2 + CH_2\text{-}CH\text{-}R'\text{-}CH\text{-}CH_2 \rightarrow$$

$$\begin{array}{cccc} | & | & | & | \\ NH & OH & OH & NH \end{array} \qquad \begin{array}{cc} \diagdown / & \diagdown / \\ O & O \end{array}$$

$$\begin{array}{cc} | & | \\ R^2 & R^2 \end{array}$$

$$CH_2\text{-}CH\text{-}R'\text{-}CH\text{-}CH_2$$

$$\begin{array}{cccc} | & | & | & | \\ NH & OH & OH & N\text{-}R_2 \end{array}$$

$$\begin{array}{cc} | & | \\ R^2 & CH_2CH\text{-}R'\text{-}CH\text{-}CH_2 \end{array}$$

$$\begin{array}{cc} | & \diagdown / \\ OH & O \end{array}$$

Second stage in "cross linking."

It is clear from these oversimplified sketches that a polyamide resin containing available primary and secondary amino groups is capable of reacting with epoxy resins and with compounds containing epoxy groups. By adjusting the ratio of amino-containing polyamide resins and epoxy resins, a series of cured products of widely varying physical properties can be obtained.

The amino-containing polyamides may also be reacted with acrylic compounds. The amino group adds to the unsaturation in the acrylic compounds producing a β-amino ethyl group. Examples of acrylic compounds which undergo such reaction are methyl acrylate, acrylonitrile, and various other acrylic esters.

$$R'NH_2 + CH_2 = CHCOOR^2 \rightarrow R'NHCH_2\text{-}CH_2COOR^2$$

With a diacrylate, a di-addition reaction can occur with the amino-containing polyamide resin to bring about crosslinking between molecules.

$$R'NH_2 + CH_2 = CHCOOR^3OOCCH = CH_2 + NH_2R' \rightarrow$$

$$R'NHCH_2CH_2COOR^3OOCCH_2CH_2NHR'$$

Some of the chemical and physical properties of a polyamide resin made by reaction of dilinoleic acid with diethylene triamine[5] are:

Acid number	0-10
Amine number	approximately 100
Molecular weight	6,000-10,000
Viscosity	10-15 poises at 150°C
Softening point (ball and ring)	-35-50°C
Solubility	
ethanol	soluble
toluene	soluble
acetone	insoluble
water	insoluble
aqueous acetic acid	soluble

The amino-containing polyamides react with acids to form amine salts and anhydrides to form amides. The latter are also formed on reaction with acid compounds, providing the reaction is carried out at a high enough temperature.

The amino-containing polyamides also react with methylol-containing products, for example, certain types of phenolic resins to produce thermoset reaction products upon heating. These reaction products, especially suitable for use as adhesives and surface coatings, have the inherent toughness and resilience of the polyamide resins and the chemical and solvent resistance of the phenolic resins if appropriate quantities of suitable materials are brought together. The nature of the reaction is not completely clear, but it is believed to proceed by condensation of amino groups of the polyamide with methylol groups of the phenolic resin.

$$-NH_2 + HOCH_2- \rightarrow -NHCH_2- + H_2O$$

The amino-containing polyamide resins will also react with formaldehyde, glyoxal and other reactive aldehydes, through an interaction of the amino groups and aldehyde groups, producing hydroxymethyl and later methylene linkages.

Cross-linking of amino-containing polyamides can thus be brought about in various ways to produce modified products which become thermoset through reaction.

Not only chemical properties but also physical properties are modified by incorporation of amino groups in the polyamide. Melting point is ordinarily lowered, solubility increased and viscosity lowered. There may also be some effect on lowering of molecular weight although in a product of this type it is difficult to be certain. A comparison of the viscosities of these products with those of linear resins containing equivalent amino and carboxyl groups shows little difference in apparent molecular weight.

Resins containing unreacted carboxyl groups can be prepared by the reverse situation in which a diamine is reacted with an excess of a tricarboxylic acid. In all such cases, as with the previous example of the trifunctional amine and dicarboxylic acid, great care must be exercised to prevent gelation during reaction. This can best be done through small-scale experiments to find the minimum excess of trifunctional material which is needed to prevent gelation from occurring.

REFERENCES

1. Ayers, C. W., *J. Appl. Chem.,* **4,** 444 (1954).
2. Baker, W. O., and Fuller, C. S., *Ann. N. Y. Acad. Sci.,* **14,** 329 (1943).
3. Bradley, T. F., and Johnston, W. B., *Ind. Eng. Chem.,* **33,** 86 (1941).
4. Cairns, T. L., *J. Am. Chem. Soc.,* **71,** 651 (1949).
5. Carothers, W. H., and Hill, J. W., *J. Am. Chem. Soc.,* **54,** 1566 (1932).

6. Carothers, W. H., *Trans. Faraday Soc.,* **32,** 39 (1936).

7. Carothers, W. H. (to Du Pont), U.S. Patent 2,071,250.

8. Cowan, J. P. (to U.S. Department of Agriculture), U.S. Patent 2,450,940, and Bradley, T. F. (to American Cyanamid Co.), U.S. Patent 2,379,413.

9. England, D. C. (to Du Pont), U.S. Patent 2,634,269.

10. Flory, P. J., *J. Am. Chem. Soc.,* **58,** 1877 (1936).

11. Floyd, D. E., Ward, W. J., and Minarik, W. L., *Modern Plastics,* **33** (11), 239 (1956).

12. Frosh, C. J. (to Bell Telephone), U.S. Patent 2,388,035.

13. Magat, E. E. (to Du Pont), U.S. Patents 2,628,216; 2,628,217; 2,628,218; and U.S. 2,628,219.

14. Mowry, J. T., and Ringwald, E. L., *J. Am. Chem. Soc.,* **72,** 4439 (1950); Magat, E. E., *et al, J. Am. Chem. Soc.,* **73,** 1031 (1951); and Ringwald, E. L. (to Du Pont), U.S. Patent 2,537,689.

15. Stastny, F., *Kunststoffe,* **40,** 273 (1950); Evans, R. D., Mighton, H. R., and Flory, P. J., *J. Am. Chem. Soc.,* **72,** 2018 (1950); Edgar, O. B., and Hill, R. J., *J. Polymer Sci.,* **3,** 609 (1948); Baker, W. O., and Fuller, C. S., *J. Am. Chem. Soc.,* **64,** 2399 (1942); and Catlin, W. E., Czerwin, E. P., and Wiley, R. H., *J. Polymer Sci.,* **2,** 412 (1947).

16. Svedberg, T., *Ind. Eng. Chem., Anal. Ed.,* **10,** 113 (1938).

17. Taylor, G. B., *J. Am. Chem. Soc.,* **69,** 635 (1947); Liquori, A. M., *J. Polymer Sci.,* **10,** 510 (1953); and Goodman, I., *J. Polymer Sci.,* **13,** 175 (1954).

4. MANUFACTURING PROCESSES FOR POLYAMIDE RESINS

The processes discussed here will be those for manufacturing polyamide resins of commercial significance. Four representative types are nylon-6,6 from hexamethylenediamine and adipic acid, nylon-6 from caprolactam, "Rilsan" from 11-amino undecanoic acid, and "Versamid" from dimerized vegetable oil acids.

Nylon-6,6

In manufacturing nylon-6,6, it is important to use as nearly as possible exact equivalents of adipic acid and hexamethylenediamine to obtain a polymer of high molecular weight. The first step involves preparation of the nylon salt by forming an aqueous solution of adipic acid and adding hexamethylenediamine to neutralize the acid, much in the manner of conducting a titration.

The nylon salts may be formed in water or aqueous alcohol solution and are crystallized from aqueous alcohol or alcohol itself. They are usually soluble in water, but insoluble in alcohol, acetone, ether, or hydrocarbons and have definite melting points as shown:

54

Diamine	Acid	M.P., °C of Salt
Tetramethylene	Azelaic	175-176
Pentamethylene	Sebacic	129-131
Hexamethylene	Adipic	183-184
Hexamethylene	Sebacic	170-172
Octamethylene	Adipic	153-154
Octamethylene	Sebacic	164-165
Dodecamethylene	Sebacic	157-158
Dodecamethylene	Adipic	144-145

The pH at neutrality (or inflection point on electrometric determination) is between 7.5 and 7.8 for most of the salts. With the nylon-6,6 salt, it is 7.63 ± 0.3. The water solution of the nylon salt is concentrated in an evaporator, then heated under pressure in an autoclave to an ultimate temperature of between 250 and 300°C while the vessel is gradually vented to allow the escape of water both from the solution and from dehydration of the salt. The salt dissociates and amide groups are formed. The latter stages of the reaction are conducted in an atmosphere of pure nitrogen or hydrogen to prevent oxidation of the resin at high temperatures.

Finally, the reaction mixture is held under reduced pressure to promote condensation, thus producing a polymer of high molecular weight.

After the polymer has been formed, it is extruded onto a casting wheel, whereupon it solidifies while being cooled with a water spray. The solid is chopped into small pieces and these are blended with chips from other production batches. The flake nylon will have a moisture content of almost one per cent at this stage.

It is also possible to prepare the polymer in an inert, high-boiling solvent such as phenol, cresol, or xylenol.[2] The solvent need not be a phenolic compound although these serve as excellent nylon solvents. The solvent is later removed, usually by distillation methods, and the polymer formed into chips, as described above.

Molecular weight of nylon-6,6 is controlled by an added chain stopper, or "stabilizer," to block off chain growth. A monobasic acid may be used for this purpose.[7]

Catalysts which may be used in nylon manufacture include oxides and carbonates of alkaline nature, halogen salts of polyvalent metals, and acids.

A flow diagram, as outlined in the Du Pont Company's brochure on "Zytel" nylon[3], showing this manufacturing process is reproduced in Figure 4.1.

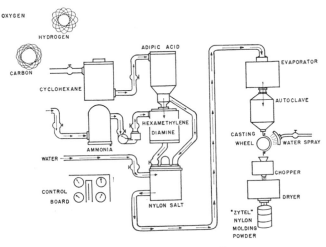

Figure 4.1. *Courtesy Du Pont Company.*

Carothers'[2] description of the nylon process does not differ in essentials from the current methods.

"The preparation of fiber-forming polyamides from the diamine-dicarboxylic acid salts can be carried out in a number of ways. The salt may be heated in the absence of a solvent or diluent (fusion method) to reaction temperature (usually 180-300°C) under conditions which permit the removal of the water formed in the reaction, until examination of the test portion indicates that the product has good fiber-forming qualities. It is desirable to subject the polyamide to reduced pressure, e.g., an absolute pressure equivalent to 50 to 300 mm of mercury, before using it in making filaments and other shaped objects. This is conveniently done by evacuating the reaction vessel in which the polyamide is prepared before allowing the polymer to solidify. Another procedure for preparing polyamides consists in heating a salt in an inert solvent for the polymer, preferably a monohydric phenol such as phenol, *m*-cresol, *o*-cresol, *p*-cresol, xylenol, *p*-butyl phenol, thymol, diphenylolpropane, and *o*-hydroxydiphenyl. With the solvents may be associated, if desired, non-solvents which are non-reactive, such as hydrocarbons, chlorinated hydrocarbons, etc. When the reaction has proceeded far enough to give a polymer of good fiber-forming qualities, the mixture can be removed from the reaction vessel and used as such (e.g., for spinning from solution) or the polymer can be separated from the solvent by precipitation, i.e., by mixing with a non-solvent for the polymer such as alcohol, ethyl acetate, or a mixture of the two. Still another method of preparation consists in heating the salt in the presence of an inert non-solvent for the polymer such as high boiling hydrocarbons of which white medicinal oil may be mentioned. The methods can also be applied directly to the diamine and dicarboxylic acid without first isolating the salt."

Nylon-6

Nylon-6 is manufactured by various procedures, one of which is as follows:

A combination of 90 parts of epsilon-caprolactam and ten parts of water plus one-tenth of one per cent of acetic acid are charged into a continuous reactor in such a way that they enter a heated zone and are held at a temperature near 250°C during polymerization. In the presence of water at high temperature, some molecules of the caprolactam are hydrolyzed to ϵ-aminocaproic acid. Following this step, other molecules of caprolactam add to the amino acid to produce a molecule of larger size. As the addition reaction proceeds, large chains are produced.

The presence of the small amount of acetic acid helps control polymer size by acting as a chain terminator. Following polymerization, the product is purified, since the mixture obtained from the continuous reactor is approximately 90 per cent polymer and 10 per cent monomeric lactam. The lactam serves to plasticize the mixture and reduces strength so that in this state the product is not suitable for fibers. The unchanged lactam can be recovered in several ways and reused. One recovery process involves leaching with hot water, in which the monomeric lactam is soluble and the polymer insoluble. This method reduces the lactam concentration to less than 5 per cent. The lactam can also be distilled out under vacuum, condensed and recovered. Scraps of polymer can be recovered and converted back to monomeric lactam for reuse. In this process the scrap is treated with super-heated steam and phosphoric acid to bring about depolymerization. The depolymerized lactam is recovered and purified by distillation.

In another process[5] for manufacturing nylon-6, molten ϵ-caprolactam, containing from one to five per cent of initiator is heated at 240 to 280°C for up to 8 hours. The initiator may be water, nylon-6,6 salt, ϵ-aminocaproic acid or another amino acid. An inert atmosphere is provided and steam is allowed to escape while polymerization proceeds. At a polymerization temperature of 265°C, an equilibrium is established in which there is 90 per cent of polymer of number average molecular weight 17,000 and 10 per cent monomer.

ε-Caprolactam can also be polymerized by the action of an alkali metal catalyst.[8]

Schrenk[9] has described a continuous process of polymerizing ε-caprolactam, in which the rate of polymerization is controlled by adjusting the thickness of layer of reaction mass. A blend of ε-caprolactam with five per cent water and 0.1 per cent phosphoric acid is introduced into the reaction chamber at a rate of 10 kg per hour. The residence time for polymerization is about 24 hours and the reaction temperature 260°C. An additional 6 hours at 240°C is allowed. A linear polyamide of intrinsic viscosity of 1.3 is discharged at the rate of 10 kg per hour from the equipment.

In continuous processes, the removal or recycling of unreacted monomer is an integral part. This is true in the manufacture of nylon-6 but not in that of nylon-6,6. According to British patents, the monomer in nylon-6 may be continuously removed by evaporation as the molten polymer is allowed to flow down a vertical wall in a thin film.[4] The residual polymer may be taken directly to the melt spinning equipment.

It has also been shown[6] that the monomer content in nylon-6 can be reduced from 10 to 11 per cent to 2 per cent or less by subjecting the molten polymer to high vacuum prior to extrusion.

The molten polymer can be formed into chips for later spinning or extrusion as with the nylon-6,6.

"Rilsan" or Polyamide-11

"Rilsan" is manufactured by the polymerization of 11-aminoundecanoic acid. The 11-aminoundecanoic acid is manufactured by reaction of undecylenic acid with ammonia. Undecylenic acid, in turn, is made by pyrolysis of methyl ricinoleate which may be obtained by alcoholysis of castor oil. The "Rilsan" polymer, therefore, is a polyamide resin, based on agricultural, renewable raw material, rather than on coal or petroleum derivatives. Polymerization is brought about by heating the monomer acid (with no other reagents) to a high temperature while distilling out the by-product water formed in the reaction. Catalysts may be added if desired. The polymerization process, therefore, is relatively simple and requires only a suitable vessel to heat materials from which by-product water is removed. The latter stages of reaction are conducted under reduced pressure to force the reaction along and produce a high molecular weight polymer. It is also important in this reaction that the starting material be relatively pure in order to obtain a substance of high molecular weight. After reaction, the molten product can be handled in one of a number of ways. As in the case of other polyamide products, it is desirable to keep it under an atmosphere of inert gas. The molten product may be extruded and formed into a ribbon from which chips may be cut off for later fabrication. However, the molten polymer may be spun directly into fibers without first forming solid chips, as with other nylons.

The polymerization reaction is carried out at a temperature slightly in excess of 200°C until the condensation is nearly complete. Both the polymer and monomer (11-amino-undecanoic acid) have a melting point of 189°C. Few or no cyclic compounds are formed in the polymerization reaction, because the large number of carbon atoms in the monomer reduce the tendency toward ring formation. No washing is required. Spinning of fibers may be conducted at nearly the same temperature as the polymerization.

The following flow sheet[1] illustrates the steps in the process.

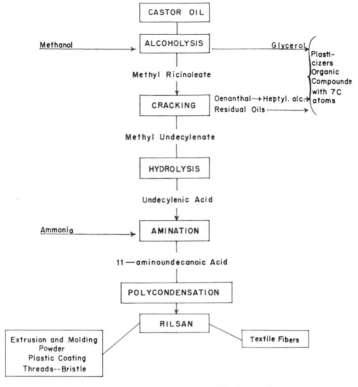

Courtesy, Leonard Hill, Ltd.

"Versamid" Polyamides

"Versamid" polyamide resins are made by the condensation of dimerized vegetable oil acids and suitable polyamino compounds. Like "Rilsan," they are based on agricultural raw materials. The method of manufacture consists of blending the ingredients at low temperature in an autoclave fitted with an efficient agitator and then raising the temperature gradually to the point where water from the reaction can be distilled off at such a rate that the distillate temperature does not go much above 100°C. When the distillation reaches the stage where it is so slow as to be negligible at a reaction temperature in the range of 150 to 250°C, vacuum may be applied in order to force the reaction to a state of advanced condensation. When the reaction is virtually complete the vacuum is released with inert gas, the product cooled slightly and drawn from the reactor in the form of a molten mass. Several grades of "Versamids" are prepared, ranging from materials which are liquid at room temperature to some which melt as high as 185°C. Naturally, handling conditions will be somewhat different for each of the various types. The liquid materials are drawn off and packaged in metal containers while the solid products may be allowed to harden in the fiber drums, or may be flaked or chipped.

General Features

Certain features are common to all processes. To get the desired molecular weight range, it is important to conduct the reaction in such a way as to remove by-products and allow the condensation to advance, or by adding a modifier to control chain size and prevent the reaction from going too far. The manufacturing processes are not highly complicated, but they do need careful control of temperature and pressure. It is also desirable to keep the reaction mixture protected from air, especially while the products are at high temperatures. Other methods employed for controlling and minimizing oxidation include addition of antioxidants and exclusion of oxygen.

The spinning process for converting polyamide resins into

filaments and yarns will be covered in the chapter on textile applications.

REFERENCES

1. Aelion, R., *Fibers Engineering and Chemistry,* **17,** 79 (1956).
2. Carothers, W. H. (to Du Pont), U.S. Patent 2,130,948.
3. General Zytel Booklet, Du Pont Company (1954).
4. Inventa, A. G., British Patents 711,956 and 716,216.
5. Joyce, R. M. (to Du Pont), U.S. Patent 2,251,519.
6. Lynch, R. T. (to American Enka Corp.), U.S. Patent 2,735,840.
7. Mersereau, H. C., *Canadian Chem. and Process Ind.,* **29,** 810 (1945).
8. Mighton, H. R. (to Du Pont Co.), U.S. Patent 2,647,105.
9. Schrenk, H. A. (to American Enka Corp.), U.S. Patent 2,735,839.

5. COATINGS AND FILMS

Polyamide resin films are used for a variety of purposes, including protection of surfaces from mechanical action such as abrasion, scratching, ordinary wear and other frictional forces; protection against the action of the elements and against chemicals and solvents; decorative effect; and corrosion inhibition.

Most polyamide resin films are either supported on some surface or are used to surround or encase another object, as in wire coatings and electrical encapsulations. Unsupported polyamide resin films similar to cellophane, "Mylar" and polyethylene films do exist but they have not yet assumed the significance of these other plastic films.

"Rilsan" Films

The "Rilsan" polyamide resins are used to some extent as free films or sheets[2] made by extrusion of the molten polymer. The sheets, either clear or colored, can be cut into strips and used in cable manufacture to replace impregnated paper; they can be treated with suitable adhesives and cut into strips to make adhesive tapes of great strength; or they can be used to prepare laminates and laminate facings, where they are especially preferred because of the resistance of the film to attack by chemicals and solvents.

"Rilsan" coatings may be applied to many different surfaces to give supported films. A flame gun is used to project the powder by air pressure through an oxyacetylene flame. The coatings are valuable for protection of electrical parts, including switch boxes and casings, especially where the parts will be subjected to corrosive forces, as in mines, ships, tropical atmospheres, and general exterior use. They may also be used on many other metallic objects where it is important to prevent corrosion.

Bacon Packaged in "Rilsan" Film.
Photograph by Photo Prismacolor. *Courtesy Societe Organico.*

The surface to which "Rilsan" is applied by flame-spraying should be dry, clean and free of grease. Otherwise, blistering and lifting of the film may take place. The coating should not be applied to porous surfaces or moisture-containing materials for similar reasons. The radius of interior angles should not be less than 5 mm. Best results are obtained by first preheating the surface of the material to be sprayed— to over 100°C for metals and to about 60°C for paper. A coating thickness of from 5 to 15 mils is preferred.

Some of the properties of "Rilsan" coatings are compared with those of nylon-6,6 coatings in Table 5.1.

TABLE 5.1. PROPERTIES OF POLYAMIDE COATINGS

Test	Units	"Rilsan" BM-D	Nylon-6,6
Density	—	1.04	1.14
Tensile strength at 73°F	psi	8,500	10,500
Elongation at 73°F	%	120	90
Modulus of elasticity at 73°F	psi	178,000	400,000
Rockwell hardness	—	R 100.5	R 118
Thermal conductivity	BTU/hr/ft²/ °F/in.	1.5	1.7
Dielectric strength (short time)	Volts/mil	430	385
Dielectric constant at 10^3 cycles	—	3.5	4.0
Moisture pickup	%	0.4	1.5
Effect of:			
Weak acids		None	None
Strong acids		Attacked	Attacked
Strong alkali		None	None
Alcohols		None	None
Esters		None	None
Hydrocarbons		None	None

Reprinted from *Modern Plastics* by permission of Breskin Publications, Inc.

If applied correctly, the "Rilsan" coating will adhere perfectly and be very resistant to mechanical shock and vibration. The smooth coating has a low frictional coefficient and, consequently, is very resistant to abrasion. Moisture pickup is less than one per cent and the coating is resistant to many chemicals and solvents. The useful temperature range for the coating is from +140°C to −60°C.

Nylon-6 Film

Nylon-6 film and laminates of nylon film with other films offer interesting possibilities. The film has good tensile and high impact strength. Tests with such film for packaging oils, fats, greases, and butter have proved successful in Europe. Blown nylon film is used to package solvents and solvent-containing materials such as caulking and putty. It may also be used for packaging foods and other items requiring exposure to boiling water temperatures. Nylon-6 film may be produced on conventional, or slightly altered, polyethylene equipment.

At comparable strengths, nylon film approximates the cost of polyethylene film. As nylon processing techniques become more widely practical, the cost of nylon film should be reduced.

According to W. H. Aikin,[1] extensive work was done in Germany during World War II on the use of polyamide resin films for repelling mustard gas. Presumably these were based on polycaprolactam. Heavy films or sheets were used in place of leather, but the toughness was only fair at low relative humidities. However, polyamides are good for cable insulation, coil forms, and wire insulation.

Other Nylon Coatings

Unsupported nylon-6,6 film is also available on a rather limited basis. As yet, no extensive uses for it exist, though its properties seem excellent, as indicated in Table 5.2 and Table 5.3.

Several interesting methods have been used for coating various articles with nylon resin. Flame-spraying was em-

ployed in the past, but more recently a whirling process is
being used. The nylon powder is held in suspension in air
inside a closed vessel by means of circulating air. The article
to be coated is heated above the melting point of the resin
and then plunged into the vessel until coated to the desired
depth.

TABLE 5.2. PHYSICAL PROPERTIES OF NYLON FILMS

	Nylon-6,6	Nylon-6,10
Thickness, mil	1-3	1-3
Yield, sq. in./#/1 mil	24,000	25,000
Specific gravity	1.14	1.09
Heat seal temperature °F	480-500	400-500
Flexlife (⅛ in. stroke)	16,000	
Water absorption % 24 hr immersion	1.5	0.4
MVTR		
gr./100 sq. in./24 hr at 100°F 90% RH		1.8
Resistance to strong acids	Fair	Fair
Resistance to strong alkalies	Excellent	Excellent
Grease and oil at room temp.	Excellent	Excellent
Grease and oil at elevated temp.	Excellent	Excellent
Organic solvents	Excellent	Excellent
Flammability	Self extinguishing	Self extinguishing

Test Methods are ASTM unless otherwise noted.
Reprinted from *Materials and Methods*, 41, (6), 93 (1955) by permission of Reinhold Publishing Corporation.

TABLE 5.3. RELATIVE PERMEABILITY OF FILMS TO GASES

Composition	Oxygen	Carbon Dioxide	Water
Nylon-6,6	36	166	—
Nylon-6,10	83	415	5.6
Polyethylene	360	1460	1.0
Saran	0.33	1.32	0.13

The "Whirlclad" process, just mentioned, was first developed in Germany, and has since been used successfully in this country for coating with a variety of powdered polymers, including nylon.[9] The article to be coated must be capable of being preheated, without distortion or decomposition, to a temperature above the melting point of the powdered polymer. Generally, the process can be used successfully to coat many metals, ceramics, glass, and even wood (if the melting point of the polymer is not too high).

Coatings of 0.010 to 0.020 inch seem to be preferable for most purposes; in some cases much thinner coatings, down to 0.002 to 0.003 inch, are desirable, since they have better wear resistance. See Figure 5.1.

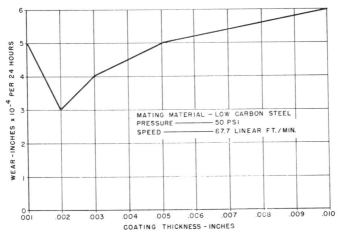

Figure 5.1. Wear of Nylon-6,6 Coating.
Reprinted from *Materials and Methods,* Volume 41, No. 6, page 93 (1955) by permission of the Reinhold Publishing Corporation.

The development of nylon coatings for metals is an attempt to take advantage of nylon's favorable frictional and

Preheated metal parts being dipped into "Whirlclad" tank containing fluidized coating powders.
Courtesy The Polymer Corporation, Reading, Pennsylvania

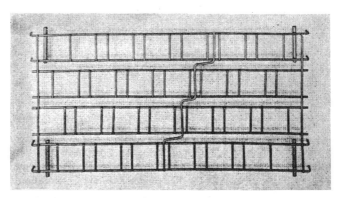

Degreasing rack coated with "Whirlsint" nylon powders by the "Whirlclad" coating process.
Courtesy Polymer Processes, Inc., Reading, Pennsylvania

wear characteristics and to minimize the effects of its dimensional instability.[9]

Test of Paints for Outboard Motors Showing Excellence of Coating from Blend of "Versamid" Polyamide and Epoxy Resins.
Courtesy General Mills, Inc.

The dimensional instability of molded parts is related to (1) moisture absorption, (2) high coefficient of thermal expansion, and (3) internal stresses.

Nylon coatings are of potential interest for many frictional applications. Field tests now cover elevator gibs, cams, rollers and bushings, locking devices, gears and bearings.

Nylon gears are well accepted where silence, ability to operate without lubrication, quick starting or stopping, or very high speeds are involved. They are made by injection molding to size or by cutting from blanks. However, many tolerance problems have been encountered in the manufacture of nylon gears, particularly in molding. The possibility of coating a metal gear with nylon is under investigation.

It is well recognized that a thin layer of nylon inside a metal shell permits better dissipation of heat and improves bearing performance.

Nylon-6,6, dissolved in creslyic acid, is used for coating magnet wire for class A usage, and is a standard item in the industry. It is thermoplastic and melts at high temperatures. Its greatest defect, however, is a tendency to absorb moisture.

The various grades of polyamide resins are all used to some extent as wire coatings materials, because of their mechanical rather than electrical properties which, however, are reasonably good. The nylon coating material may be made up in the form of an extruded tubular sheath for the wire or may be extruded directly on the wire from the molten material.

Vegetable Oil Polyamides

The polyamide resins made from vegetable oil dimers are soluble in alcohols and in alcohol-hydrocarbon mixtures. They may be used alone or with plasticizers or other modifiers as surface coatings. In this form they are employed most frequently as coatings for flexible substrates, including paper, cellophane and aluminum foil.

Their greatest attraction lies in their heat-seal and grease and water-barrier properties. Frequently they are used for the combination of all these properties. The soluble polyamides are applied over printed matter on packages as gloss overprint varnishes to protect the printing against abrasion and effects of oil or water, as well as to enhance appearance by improving gloss and depth of color.

Data on moisture vapor permeability and certain heat-sealing properties are given[1] in Tables 5.4 and 5.5.

TABLE 5.4. MOISTURE VAPOR TRANSFER PROPERTIES OF "VERSAMID" 940 AND 950 — COATED GLASSINE IN COMPARISON WITH OTHER BARRIER MATERIALS

Material	Approximate M.V.T.* in g/sq meter/24 hrs	
	Flat	Fold
Glassine, single sheet, uncoated	3000	3000
Glassine, single, waxed	0.2-0.8	18-20
Glassine, single, 6-12 lb per ream on both sides with "Versamid" 940	100	—
Glassine, single, double coat of "Versamid" 950, 2.5 lb per ream on both sides	6-7.5	12-15
Glassine, paraffin laminated, double coat of "Versamid" 950 at 1.4 lb per ream on both sides	0.55	0.84
Kraft Paper, uncoated	1250	1250
Cellophane, untreated	500	500

* TAPPI Test 448-M-41 at 73°F and 50% relative humidity.

TABLE 5.5. SEAL PROPERTIES OF "VERSAMIDS"

	% Retention of Seal at:			Blocking,* %		
	−20°F	40°F	80°F	Face to Face	Face to Back	Sealing Range
"Versamid" 940 (coated at 4 lbs/ream)	40	40	90	0	0	80-110°C

* Blocking tendency was determined on storage at 60°C for 24 hrs at 75% relative humidity in accord with TAPPI Test T-447-in-47. The grease resistance of the "Versamid" 940 film, conducted in accord with TAPPI Test T-454-m-44 is greater than 1800 seconds.

If properly pigmented and formulated with other materials, the alcohol-soluble polyamides based on vegetable oil fatty acids may be incorporated into inks. These inks are of the aniline or rotogravure type, and have many of the same properties as the clear coatings and heat-seal adhesives, i.e., high gloss, heat resistance, resistance to water, greases and oils, good appearance and alcohol solubility. Such alcohol-soluble materials do not harm rubber rollers frequently used on coating machines. They are especially suited for printing on polyethylene packages.

Because the films used for most packaging are only two- or three-thousandths of an inch thick, they do not have enough "give" for smooth printing from hard metal plates. Special flexographic printing from rubber plates is preferred. However, ordinary oils swell and rot these rubber plates. Because the ink cannot penetrate the plastic films, the oil-base inks also dry too slowly for rapid printing. Alcohol-base inks are invariably used for the flexographic process.

Crush Test on Toothpaste Tubes Coated with "Versamid" Epoxy Enamel.
Courtesy General Mills, Inc.

The only satisfactory natural printing-ink resin that will dissolve in alcohol is shellac, which is brittle, shows poor resistance to water and will not stick to many plastic surfaces.

The same qualities that have made "Versamids" valuable in adhesives, paints and lacquers enables them to hold the pigments in inks for packaging materials firmly in place. They have excellent wetting ability and convert easily into solids; these solids have high tensile strengths and yet are flexible enough to withstand twisting and stretching without losing their grip.

Thermoset Resin Alloys—Polyamide and Epoxy Resin Blends

All the coating materials discussed thus far are of the thermoplastic type which can be melted and remelted. There is also another class of coating materials of a thermosetting type which may be prepared from the polymerized vegetable oil polyamides. These coatings are made from a type of "Versamid" polyamide which contains free amino groups and which is very reactive with epoxy resins. Combinations of the amino-containing polyamide resins with epoxy resins and with phenolic resins make possible coating vehicles which can be applied from solvent mixtures by brushing, spraying or dipping. Films of such materials are resistant to chemicals, solvents, heat and water. By virtue of the inherent corrosion resistance of the polyamide itself, such films also offer excellent protection against corrosion for iron and steel materials.

Where blends of polyamide and epoxy resins are used, usual practice is to prepare solutions of the resins separately to form concentrates, to combine the concentrates and to reduce the viscosity of the mixture with thinners to proper application viscosity. The solvents most often used for the polyamide part of the system are mixtures of alcohols and

TABLE 5.6. PROPERTIES OF TYPICAL FULLY CURED FILMS
(Cured at 300°F for 20 minutes)

Composition	Hardness	Flexibility (Mandrel Passed) in.	Impact Resistance on Steel (in.-lb.)	Abrasion Resistance (g loss) [a]	Alkali Resistance [b]	Acid Resistance [c] 20% Acetic	Acid Resistance [c] 50% H_2SO_4	Solvent Resistance Toluene	Solvent Resistance 50% Ethyl Alcohol	Solvent Resistance High Test Gasoline	Boiling Water Resistance (30 min.)
"Epon" 1001-"Versamid" 100											
40:60	34	1/8		0.0073	OK	OK	OK	S	S	OK	S(rec.) [d]
50:50	56	1/8	172	0.0054	OK	OK	OK	S	S	OK	OK
60:40	62	1/8		0.0035	OK	OK	OK	S	S	OK	OK
"Epon" 1001-"Versamid" 100											
40:60	44	1/8		0.0115	OK	OK	OK	S	S	OK	OK
50:50	57	1/8	172	0.0074	OK	OK	OK	S	S	OK	OK
60:40	57	1/8		0.0011	OK	OK	OK	S	S	OK	OK
"Epon" 864-"Versamid" 100											
50:50	41	1/8	172	0.0019	OK	OK	OK	S	S	OK	S(rec.)
60:40	49	1/8		0.0121	OK	OK	OK	S	S	OK	S(rec.)

[a] Weight loss (g) 500 cycles, 1 kg. No. 10 wheel.
[b] Observed after 3 days immersion in 20% NaOH at 170° and 212°F.
[c] Films held for 7 days at room temperature and then immersed for 1 day in test liquid.
[d] rec. = recovered within 1 hour.

hydrocarbons; for example, for a rapidly evaporating solvent, a mixture of isopropyl alcohol and toluene is often used. For a more slowly evaporating solvent, as might be used in general purpose spraying, a blend of one part cellosolve and nine parts of xylene may be used. For a very slowly evaporating system, such as might be used in brushing, high-boiling aromatic naphthas should be substituted for the xylene. The epoxy resin portion is dissolved in a mixture of ketone and aromatic hydrocarbon such as methyl isobutyl ketone and xylene.

Pigmentation can be conducted in the customary manner using ball mills, roller mills or other grinding devices to prepare fine pigment dispersions. Both resins provide excellent wetting media and serve well for grinding of pigments. Because of the higher viscosity of the polyamide solution, pigment grinding is often done in this vehicle by means of a roller mill. All the common types of pigments may be satisfactorily handled. These include carbon blacks, titanium dioxide, chrome yellow, phthalocyanine greens and blues, toluidine red, red lead, and zinc chromate. It is not necessary to pigment both parts of the vehicle. Pigmentation of either one is sufficient, if followed by addition of the other portion of the vehicle and thinner just before the material is to be applied. Such coatings have very high gloss and an unusual degree of hardness and flexibility or impact resistance.[5] Solvent resistance and the chemical resistance are also excellent. Some of these properties are illustrated in Table 5.6.

Studies of weathering resistance made by means of a Weather-ometer and outdoor exposure tests at various locations have shown that films of polyamide and epoxy resin compositions have excellent durability. They show little tendency to check and crack, and have excellent color retention. The films will fail over a long period of time by gradual erosion or chalking.[5] Actually the rate of chalking is probably a little greater than for some of the more conventional coating materials such as alkyd resins. However, the durability is better and beneath the chalked surface one finds a glossy, intact coating film. See Table 5.7.

TABLE 5.7. COMPARISON OF AIR-DRIED COATINGS—TYPICAL VALUES

	"Epon" 1001: Ethylene-diamine (100:6)	"Versamid" 100: "Epon" 1001 (50:50)	"Versamid" 115: "Epon" 1001 (50:50)	"Versamid" 115: "Epon" 1001 (35:65)
Dry tack-free	130 min.	65 min.	80 min.	80 min.
Initial gloss of white enamel	90	102	102	103
Gloss after 300 hr in Weather-ometer	65	93	81	73
Gloss after 500 hr in Weather-ometer	5	36	30	12
Initial light reflection (Hunter-Green filter)	77.0	77.4	76.4	—
Yellowness-initial (Hunter A-B-G)	1.4	3.6	2.1	—
After 300 hr in Weather-ometer	11.8	9.4	10.2	—
Chalking after 3000 hrs in Weather-ometer	Heavy	Medium	Medium	Medium
Boiling water 7 hr	OK	OK	OK	OK
20% NaOH—1 day	Hard	Hard	Hard	Hard
50% H_2SO_4—1 day	Hard	Hard	Soft	Soft
Sward hardness:				
1 day	28	24	26	33
1 week	42	48	50	59
1 month	47	50	50	—
Impact resistance (in.-lb) tin plates:				
1 day	30+	2	30+	30+
1 week	30+	30+	30+	30+

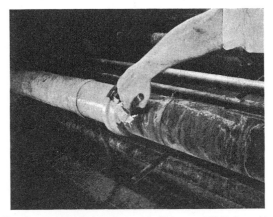

Coating Damp Steel Pipe with "Versamid" Polyamide
and Epoxy Resin Paint.
Courtesy General Mills, Inc.

Exposure Testing of Paints Made of Blended "Versamid"
Polyamide and Epoxy Resins.
Courtesy General Mills, Inc.

Films of polyamides and of the blends of polyamide and epoxy resin systems do not readily transmit moisture vapor. This can be seen from the following table of moisture vapor permeability values as determined by the Payne cup procedure. Specific permeability, defined by H. F. Payne, is shown for several materials below.[7]

Coatings	Specific Permeability
Linseed oil[3]	3.0
Clear varnish[3]	1.0
"Versamid" 100/Epon 1001 (50:50)	0.28
"Versamid" 115/Epon 1001 (35:65)	0.32

$$\text{Specific permeability} = \text{weight} \frac{H_2O \text{ lost in mg} \times \text{mm thickness}}{10 \text{ sq cm}}$$

Because of the fact that "Versamid"-epoxy resin alloy coatings are corrosion inhibitors and excellent wetting agents, they may be applied over wet surfaces by brushing. Apparently the action of brushing causes water on the surface of the material being coated to become emulsified in the coating. When the coating dries, the water is carried out along with the solvent leaving a coating which is virtually the same as that obtained on a dry surface. The "Versamid"-epoxy coatings are used on dairy equipment, oil well riggings, freight car interiors, water softeners, industrial equipment, chemical laboratory equipment, pipelines and general maintenance finishes. They will adhere to metals, wood, rubber, masonry and plastics with few exceptions.

Polyamide and Phenolic Resin Blends

Also of considerable importance and interest are coatings made from combinations of polyamide resins of the amino-containing type and certain types of phenolic resins. The reaction here is between amino groups of the polyamide and methylol groups of the phenolic resins. The reaction forms a new carbon to nitrogen bond which links a molecule of one resin with a molecule of the other resin and releases a molecule of by-product water. This is in contrast to the epoxy resin reaction which forms no volatile by-product.

Three test discs of Plaskon Nylon 8200, each graduated in thickness (.020, .045, and .070″) showing control of crystallinity with quench temperatures from 60 to 200°F. This unusual property permits the extrusion of clear nylon film.

Courtesy Barrett Division, Allied Chemical and Dye

Table 5.8. Properties of "Versamid" Resin—Phenolic Resin Coatings*

| Composition Solids Basis** | Viscosity | Rocker Hardness | Impact Resistance (in.-lb) | Solvent Resistance 120°F for 48 hr | | | Oleic Acid | Water | Boiling Water (2 hr) | Chemical Resistance Room Temp. (1 day) | |
				Acetone	Toluene	95% Alcohol				20% NaOH	37% H$_2$SO$_4$
60% "Versamid" 100 40% BLL-3913 (Bakelite)	F	56	16-30	S	S	H	H	H	H	H	H
50% "Versamid" 125 50% BLL-3913 (Bakelite)	C	58	2-4	H	H	H	H	H	H	H	H
45% "Versamid" 115 55% P97 (Monsanto)	N	68	16-30	S	H	H	H	H	H	H	H
50% "Versamid" 115 50% CLS-3112 (Bakelite)	L	66	60+	S	H	S	H	H	H	H	H
55% "Versamid" 125 45% BKS-2710 (Bakelite)	E	60	4-8	H	H	H	H	H	H	H	H
55% "Versamid" 115 45% BKS-2710 (Bakelite)	G	58	30-60	SS	H	SS	H	H	H	H	H
45% "Versamid" 115 55% Varcum 5301	C	58	16-30	SS	H	H	H	H	H	H	H
BKS-2600 alone (Bakelite)	F	72	Fail ¼ in. rod bend	H	H	H	H	H	H	Wr.	H

* Dry films of about 0.4 mil thickness (1.5 mil wet film—doctor blade applied) on tin plate or glass from 40% nonvolatile solutions and baked 15 minutes at 400°F were used in these evaluations.
** The phenolic resins were used as alcohol solutions and the "Versamids" were used as solutions in xylene-cellosolve, 9:1. Reduction to 40% nonvolatile was accomplished with xylene and a minimum of alcohol or cellosolve. Further reduction to spraying viscosity can be made with xylene-butanol, 1:1.
H = hard. SS = slightly soft. S = soft. VS = very soft, Wr. = wrinkled. Hardness was judged by finger nail scratch immediately on withdrawal of panel from liquid. Hardness was regained quickly as solvent evaporated.

It also differs in other ways, one of the principal ones being the long pot life at ordinary storage temperatures. Blends of polyamide resins and heat reactive phenolic resins in solution may be stored for periods of several months before appreciable change in viscosity or of coating properties is noticed. Thus, they have uses not possible with the polyamide and epoxy coating systems. Another difference is that the polyamide-epoxy resin system will cure at room temperature or at temperatures as low as 50°F and at elevated temperatures, while polyamide-phenolic resin compositions require baking at temperatures of 300°F and higher to give the best results.

Films cast and baked from blends of polyamide resins and suitable heat reactive phenolic resins have the extremely good chemical and solvent resistance of the phenolic resins and the flexibility, impact resistance, and alkali resistance of the polyamide resins.[6] Because of this unusual combination of good properties, they offer promise as coatings materials for lining of tanks, drums, cans and pails. These coating systems, because of their dark colors, are not as well suited for decorative finishes in appliance enamels, automotive paints and the like. In fact, they are less seldom pigmented than are the polyamide and epoxy resin coating systems. When pigmented it is more for the purpose of obtaining the protective than decorative effect. Some of the comparative data for films from interaction of polyamide and phenolic resins are shown in Table 5.8.

Coating Methods

Films from systems made up of polyamide and epoxy resin combinations may be applied by most of the common coating methods, i.e., by spraying, dipping, brushing, roll coating, or knife coating. In dipping tanks one must be careful not to exceed the pot life of the material, especially if a continuous system of introducing coating material for dipping is employed. Straight polyamide resin coatings are applied by hot-melt techniques by dipping, roller coating or knife coating, or they may be applied from solution by spraying, brushing, dipping, roller coating, or knife coating. Coatings comprised of polyamide resin and phenolic resin mixtures are usually applied by spraying or roller coating although other systems of application are ordinarily satisfactory.

"Versamid" polyamide films, because of their good elongation, excellent flexibility and adhesion to a variety of surfaces, may be used for numerous coatings purposes. These include barrier coatings for paper to prevent attack by moisture, or grease, as have been mentioned for heat-seal surface coatings, and coatings for materials and plastic surfaces.

The blend of "Versamid" and epoxy resins has unusually good adhesion to plastic surfaces and to many different metals. It may be used on steel, iron, copper, brass, tin, aluminum, galvanized iron, magnesium and other metals; and on "Saran," "Mylar," cellophane, glassine, rigid vinyls, cellulosic plastics, polystyrene, acrylic resins, polyester resins, cured phenolic resins and melamine-formaldehyde resins.

Summary

Development of free, unsupported films of polyamides is still in the beginning stages, but growth of uses seems likely, particularly if costs can be reduced. The films are especially attractive for tapes, packaging and cable insulation. At this stage, nylon-6 and "Rilsan" are receiving the greatest attention.

Thermoplastic polyamide resins may be coated on magnet

wire and electronics parts as well as on many metallic articles. The soluble and lower melting types are used as overprint varnishes, heat-seal coatings, ink vehicles, and barrier coatings.

Thermoset resin alloys made from blends of amino-containing "Versamid" polyamide resins and epoxy resins have established themselves as maintenance coatings for use where chemical resistance, durability, and corrosion resistance are important.

The thermoset resin alloys made from blends of amino-containing "Versamid" polyamide resins and heat reactive phenolic resins show considerable promise as chemical and solvent resistant baking finishes, can and drum linings, wire coatings, and coatings for industrial articles.

Future developments in the field of coatings and films for polyamide resin compositions seem assured.

REFERENCES

1. Aiken, W. H., *Plastics,* **7,** (2), 36 (1947).
2. Dumon, R., *Modern Plastics,* **33,** (12), 230 (1956).
3. Dunn, E. J., *Official Digest,* **24,** 365 (1952).
4. General Mills Technical Bulletin 11-B (1955).
5. General Mills Technical Bulletin 11-D-1 (1955).
6. Glaser, D. W., Ling, R., Peerman, D. E., and Floyd, D. E., *Official Digest,* **29,** 476 (1957).
7. Payne, H. F., *Official Digest,* **11,** 297 (1939); *Ind. Eng. Chem.,* **2,** 737 (1940).
8. Renfrew, M. M., Wittcoff, H., Floyd, D. E., and Glaser, D. W., *Ind. Eng. Chem.,* **46,** 2226 (1954).
9. L. L. Stott, *Materials and Methods,* **41,** (6), 93 (1955); *Org. Finishing,* June, 1956. Process may be practised under license from Polymer Processes, Inc., Reading, Pa.

6. POLYAMIDE FIBERS

Increased industrialization has brought demands for more and better functional fibers just as it has called for better metals, plastics and coatings. In this chapter, the developmental uses of polyamide resins in the fiber and textile fields will be emphasized.

It may be helpful here to divide polymers into three classes —rubber-like polymers, amorphous polymers, and fiber-forming polymers. In rubber-like polymers forces between adjacent polymer chains are weak and the chains themselves are quite flexible; if the chains are of sufficient length, a rubber-like state can be achieved. The amorphous or glass-like polymers have chains which are not very flexible, or else their intermolecular forces are stronger than those of rubber-like polymers. Many plastics belong to this class. Chain structure of the crystalline or fiber-forming polymer is quite regular and symmetrical, and this permits crystallization. Such polymers have strong hydrogen bonding and other intermolecular forces.

Early Development

It is important to understand that there are three types of fibers: the natural fibers, including wool, cotton, and silk; the artificial fibers, such as viscose rayon, cuprammonium rayon, cellulose acetate, and regenerated protein fibers; and the synthetic fibers, including nylon, "Dacron," "Vinyon" and "Dynel." Artificial fibers are chemical modifications of natural products.

For about 25 years, the idea dominating research on synthetic fibers had been the duplication of natural fibers, with special emphasis on silk and wool. This was especially noticeable in the development of nylon fibers. The similarity between the physical properties of nylon and silk or nylon and wool is very great; all three fibers are strong, tough, and resistant to chemicals. More remarkable, however, is the degree of similarity in their chemical composition—all three belong to the general class of polyamide polymers. Nylon is a polymer with recurring amide groups spaced so that it is possible to obtain a good deal of intermolecular hydrogen bonding. Silk and wool are polymers of natural proteins which also contain amide groups and which are also capable of a high degree of hydrogen bonding. The differences between synthetic nylon and natural wool and silk will be pointed out later in this chapter.

In the early development of artificial fibers, rayon fibers were among the first to be studied. Although rayons are based upon a natural product, there is enough chemical modification to class the various types as artificial fibers. As early as 1930 the critical factors needed in a fiber to be used for reinforcement of automobile tires were being seriously studied. It was learned that a fiber must possess high tensile strength, toughness, fatigue resistance and capability of being made into thinner, more flexible reinforcement for rubber. By 1934, research at the Du Pont Company had resulted in the formation of "Cordura" high tenacity rayon to be used in automobile tires and for other industrial applications.

The development of this fiber not only helped satisfy the industrial requirements of a specific segment of the industry,

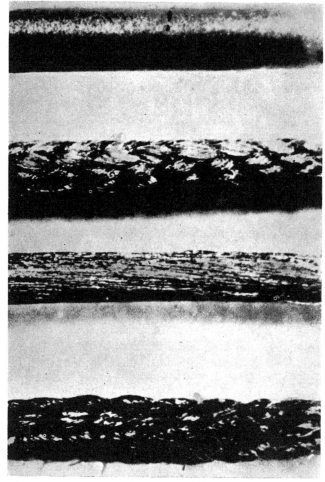

These enlarged sections show the difference in structure and appearance between a surgical suture of nylon monofilament (top), and ones of silk. Smooth, solid nylon is stronger and less irritating than silk to the body's tissues. Nylon filaments are used also for fishing leaders, and all types of brush bristles.

Courtesy Du Pont Co.

but also brought about an awareness of the need for more research in the field of fibers.

In consumer items, a similar awakening occurred in the late 1920's and early 1930's. For example, it had been known that rayon and acetate were useful fibers for making lingerie and dresses, but most women thought that rayon hosiery was not satisfactory because of poor durability. Research was directed toward developing derivatives of cellulose which might make better fibers for hosiery. Some degree of success was achieved, although it soon became apparent that the approach would not be entirely successful because only slight modification was possible if one was to preserve the essential structural features of the cellulose used as raw material.

At about this time, at the Du Pont Laboratories W. H. Carothers and co-workers began research on the general field of synthetic polymers. The history of that development, how it resulted in the formation of a series of polyamide resins known as nylon, and what has become of them has been treated in previous chapters.

Nylon, alone among synthetic fibers, gained commercial acceptance before World War II. In fact, its acceptance as a fibrous material for making hosiery was almost immediate after its introduction. The first plant began manufacturing operations in 1939 and by 1941 production had increased some 170 per cent beyond the production of the year before. Most of the nylon produced went into hosiery manufacture although in 1940 it also won acceptance for a number of miscellaneous applications such as monofilaments for rackets, insulation for electrical wires, and fibers for parachute safety belts, straps and cords. By building new plants and enlarging the capacity of the existing plants, output was increased. Late in 1941 when an embargo was placed on silk, facilities for manufacture of nylon yarn multiplied. Substantial increases were also made in 1942 and 1943 with almost the entire output of nylon going into military items.

Later, nylon filaments helped to relieve a shortage of pig bristles formerly imported from the Orient for many types of brushes. New bristles made with a taper were developed by pulling the filaments from the spinneret at varying rates of speed. Although output increased still further by 1944, the demand was such that all nylon remained under allocation. With the end of the war in 1945 and cancellation of government orders, production of nylon for civilian uses was resumed.

The paintbrush with natural bristle (left) and the one with new tapered nylon bristles (right) have been used the same length of time. Tapered nylon wears at least three times longer than natural bristle.

Courtesy Du Pont Co.

Encouraged by the reception given nylon, the textile industry asked for new types of synthetic fibers. Since then "Orlon," "Acrylan," "Dynel," "Dacron," and, in the last few years, other synthetic fibers have been introduced.

Fiber Usage

World fiber consumption tends to exceed production facilities. In fact, the supply of natural fibers themselves would be inadequate if synthetic and artificial fibers had not been available. Total consumption of textile fibers in this country in 1952 was 6½ billion pounds or about 40 pounds per person. This includes 27 pounds of cotton, 9 pounds of rayon and synthetics, and 4 pounds of wool. The synthetic fiber consumption in 1952 amounted to 275 million pounds or about four per cent of all fibers consumed. The rayon consumption amounted to about 19 per cent of the total. It is predicted that by 1960, 975 million pounds of synthetics will be needed and, in 1975, four billion pounds of synthetics, including 1.2 billion pounds of acrylic, one billion pounds of polyesters, one billion pounds of miscellaneous material and 800 million pounds of nylon. Although the synthetic fibers have in many instances replaced natural fibers, there is certainly a place for both.

Nylon versus Natural Fibers

Silk is still an excellent fiber, but it costs about four dollars per pound. Cotton and wool are also excellent fibers and their more reasonable prices account for the great production and consumption of both materials. There are other differences, too; for example, silk is a continuous filament fiber and wool a staple fiber. If nylon is to compete with these materials, at least two grades must be available.

Nylon cannot be dyed as easily as viscose rayon, cotton or wool. However, techniques have been worked out permitting use of acetate, acid, and chrome dyes as well as some direct, vat, azoic, and basic colors.[8] Nylon has good chemical stability although its strength decreases gradually upon exposure to sunlight. Continuous filament nylon has a cold feel to the skin and some types of fabric have a limp hand. It offers problems in soiling, localized melting, flammability, and static electrification and wicking. It has little or no felting properties (which can constitute either a virtue or a deficiency). Nylon has largely supplanted silk but it is doubtful that it will replace wool or cotton unless the price is reduced appreciably.

Formation of Nylon Threads

Mr. H. C. Mersereau[12] has described formation of threads from nylon.* In this process, there are two phases, the first of which involves melting the flakes of nylon and, the second, extruding or spinning the melt in the form of a yarn. When the molten plastic material has been stretched under properly controlled conditions, it assumes an elastic form and becomes a true textile fiber which can then be wound for appropriate package shipment.

The nylon flakes are melted by heating them in an atmosphere of nitrogen gas to temperatures near 300°C. The molten nylon is forced with high pressure through a sand-packed filter at a temperature the same as that of the molten nylon, maintained by a jacketed heating unit. After passing through the sand, the molten nylon goes through the spinneret, a metal plate in which holes of one/one-hundredths of an inch in diameter are drilled. The nylon is extruded

---

* By permission of *Canadian Chemical Processing.*

Melt Spinning of "Rilsan" Fibers
Courtesy Societe Organico

through these holes (which are separated as widely as the spinneret size will permit) into the open air where it is immediately cooled to prevent charring at the high temperature. Cooling is accomplished by passing a current of cold air across the line of travel. The filaments are extruded at a rate of about 1,000 feet per minute but are drawn away from the spinneret surface at speeds greatly in excess of this with the result that at the moment of transition between the molten and solid state the diameter of the filament is greatly reduced. This results in a reduction of the weight or denier of the yarn and also brings about orientation of the fibers of the molten yarn. At this stage the fibers are stretched about fourfold.

The number of filaments in a yarn is determined by the number of holes in the spinneret. In general, each filament is equivalent to about three denier and consequently the number of filaments in any nylon yarn can be roughly determined by dividing its denier by three. Thus, for example, 30 denier yarn, hosiery count, contains ten filaments. The filaments are drawn away from the spinneret face and passed through a device known as the convergence guide which unites them into a single thread. The yarn then goes through a long tube in which it is bathed in steam to absorb static electricity and to bring it into approximate equilibrium with the moisture of the air. Nylon is not noticeably hygroscopic, but it requires this state of equilibrium if operating difficulties are to be avoided. The yarn is now passed over a finish roll which applies a material that cements the filaments into a thread, thus preventing separation and damage and also eliminating static electricity in a better way than did the steam conditioning. The yarn passes over rolls which give it power for drawing away from the spinneret. After this, it is wound on a bobbin and the first stage of the yarn manufacture has been completed.

Unoriented yarn is still not a textile fiber but can readily be made so by converting it from a plastic condition to an elongated condition. This is done by stretching it to about 3½ to 4½ times its original length. The roll holding the

Spools of "Rilsan" Yarn
Courtesy Societe Organico

yarn is operated at a given speed and the rewind is operated approximately four times as fast, which tends to stretch the yarn about fourfold. The filaments, as first extruded before orientation, are believed to have a relatively random condition of molecular orientation. As the yarn is stretched, the diameter is reduced and the molecules tend to arrange themselves parallel to the fiber axis and to pack in a tighter bundle. The yarn is elongated and oriented and becomes much stronger. The machine used to stretch the yarn is called a draw twister.

The bobbin of yarn taken from the spinning machine is placed on a creel on the top of the machine and the yarn is drawn over a series of tension guides through a pair of rollers which control speed. The yarn next passes around a snubbing pin which serves to localize the drawing. It is passed three times around a driven roll assembly which is geared to a surface gear rotating at approximately four times the speed of the driven roll. After drawing, the yarn is wound on a standard ring rail device which, in addition to providing a wind up package for the yarn, also adds a certain amount of twist to prevent the filaments from becoming separated.

Like silk, nylon is coated with a sizing agent to facilitate handling. The sizing may be accomplished before or after the yarn is shipped to the user. Various compositions have been used to make sizing materials, one of which is a proprietary material containing polyvinyl alcohol.

Similar processes may be used for extruding nylon into coarser monofilaments for use as bristles and for other applications. The monofilaments can be obtained in diameters ranging from 2 mils to 5 mils by progressively varying the takeoff speed during extrusion. This process may also be employed to obtain the tapered bristles especially desired for brushes.

Filaments are improved by cold drawing which changes their internal structure.[14] Neither heat, solvents nor plasticizers is necessary for this process, but wetting with water reduces breakage. In its usual form, nylon is strong, lustrous, and resembles silk. But wool-like fibers may be produced by carding and steaming under 25 pounds of pressure for five minutes, whereby a permanent crimp is given to the filaments. Crimping may also be accomplished by passing the filaments through heated intermeshing gears, pressing them into racks, and many other mechanical and chemical methods. Fibers of nylon-6,6 are characterized by excellent appearance, high elastic recovery, great wet strength and insolubility in most common reagents, except phenol and formic acid.

The cross sections of synthetic fibers tend to be uniform and regular in shape. Those prepared by melt spinning are ordinarily round. Natural fibers may have almost any cross-sectional appearance, although their shape also tends to be regular.

Among the fibers which are produced by melt spinning are nylon-6,6, "Perlon L," saran, polyethylene, "Dacron" or "Terylene," and some cellulose esters.

It is desirable that the minimum softening or melting point of fibers exceed the highest temperature at which they will be used. Therefore, it is preferable that a fiber not soften at a temperature below 200°C, although a number of commercial fibers do soften at lower temperatures.

Fiber Structure

Polymeric materials are suitable for a variety of uses. For example, a polyamide resin may be used as a fiber or a molding compound. However, the properties required for different applications are not the same. A material to be used as a molding compound should have low moisture absorption. It is often desirable in a plastic to have a rather low melting point for ease of handling. In molding compounds, while a resin of great strength may not be required, the finished article should be fairly strong. On the other hand, plastic materials for making fibers should have high melting points and relatively high water absorption. It is also absolutely necessary that these materials have great strength.

The term "denier," first used in the silk industry before artificial fibers were known, is a unit of fiber size. Specifically, it is the weight in grams of a length of filament of 9,000 meters. Tenacity, on the other hand, is a measure of strength expressed as number of grams of load required to break one denier filament. For example, if a peak load of 250 grams will just break a 100 denier yarn, the tenacity may be said to be 2½ grams per denier. High tenacity fibers such as nylon may reach values as high as 6 to 7 grams per denier.

Elongation at the breaking point tests how far a fiber may be stretched before it is parted. Elasticity, on the other hand, measures the recovery of a fiber to its original condition after stretching. It is highly possible that a fiber of long elongation will have poor elasticity and the reverse may also be true. If a fiber stretched ten per cent, for example, a fiber 100 inches long pulled to 110 inches, returns to its original length when released, the elastic recovery will be 100 per cent. If it returns to 102 inches, then it has shown only 80 per cent elastic recovery. Fibers ordinarily have high elasticity for low stretches, but not nearly as good elasticity for high stretches.

Nylon yarns are manufactured in the denier range of 20 to 210 and in a range of filament denier of one to 630 or higher. The tenacities range from 4½ to 8 grams per denier depending upon the type of yarn. The elongation of the yarn can be varied from 12 per cent to about 100 or 200 per cent and, for special applications, undrawn yarn capable of being elongated 400 to 500 per cent can be obtained.

When stretched, drawn nylon filaments will recover about 50 per cent almost immediately, nearly 85 per cent complete after one day and completely after about two weeks. The ability of nylon to stretch and its rate of recovery are somewhat dependent upon relative humidity. For example, at zero per cent relative humidity, the tension required for a one per cent elongation is about 0.5 gram per denier, whereas at 50 per cent relative humidity, it is only 0.3 gram per denier, and at 100 per cent it is 0.12 gram per denier.

A property common to all fibers is the high ratio of length to diameter. For example, the typical length of a cotton fiber is one inch, wool three inches, and flax one inch. Typical diameters are: cotton 0.0007 inch, wool 0.001 inch, and flax 0.0009 inch. Thus, the ratio of length to diameter is 1400 for cotton, 3000 for wool and 1200 for flax.

The cross section of fibers may take any shape; some are circular, as is generally the case with melt-spun fibers and some have a dumbbell or dog-bone shape. The shape of the cross sections of the fiber is not nearly as important as is the uniformity or regularity of shape; those of the artificial fibers are usually regular. Yarns having circular fibers are soft, but they have poor covering power probably because a circular cross section offers the minimum surface for a given volume. Among natural fibers, wool is probably the most important one having a circular cross section. It is interesting to note that nylon of similar chemical structure also has a circular cross section.

The flatter fibers have a high luster and excellent covering power, but a rather rough quality probably due somewhat to the flat filament cross section. The greater the flatness of the fiber, the better is the absorption of dyestuff; the circular fibers are more difficult to dye. Some fibers have a lobed cross-sectional appearance and some a serrated appearance.

Ordinarily, the finer the filament, the softer it will be; and, the coarser or larger the filament, the stiffer and harder it will feel. For this reason, most yarns are composed of a large number of fine filaments twisted together to give a thread, rather than only a few coarser filaments.

The synthetic fibers generally have average molecular weights in the region of 12,000 to 20,000. If molecular weight is below 4,000, little or no fiber-forming properties exist. The material is weak and cannot be made into a filament of length. Between 4,000 to 6,000, it is possible to make fibers but they are very weak and brittle. In the range of 6,000 to 8,000, the fibers are better but still very weak. At 8,000 to 10,000, a marked improvement is shown in fiber formation and fiber strength.

Since the strength of a fiber molecule is along its chain, if the fiber is unoriented, strength along the fiber axis direction will be no greater than in other directions. While some polymer molecules are rigid and rod-like, as in cellulose, others are coiled and highly flexible as in the polyamide molecules. The coiled or flexible type of chain can be readily oriented through cold drawing, thus greatly increasing strength in the direction of the axis. The orientation, of course, is the result of secondary valence forces.

The secondary valence forces, largely hydrogen bonds, which orient polyamide molecules, serve, in a sense, as weak cross-links. When a rubber-like molecule is stressed, the cross-linking bonds tend to bring it back to its original random, disordered condition. A stressed or drawn, oriented polyamide molecule is brought back to its original condition by hydrogen bonds. But, since these are weaker than the cross-linking bonds they bring the molecule back more slowly. If enough original stress is applied, the weak hydrogen bonds are loosened and the polymer goes through what is called the yield point. At this point, it does not break or fail but slippage occurs so that the weak hydrogen bonds are broken and new ones can be formed between polar groups at different chain locations.

During drawing, the molecules become increasingly oriented parallel to the fiber axis. Coiled molecules tend to become straighter. Molecules under greatest stress originally break the secondary valence bonds connecting them to their molecular neighbors and move so as to release the stress. Creep has been greatly reduced or eliminated. On further extension, a distortion of primary valence bonds occurs, which leads to eventual molecular fracture.

Nylon-6,6 is melt-spun at 265°C or higher. Because of its tendency to discolor in air at this temperature, the spinning is accomplished in an oxygen-free atmosphere such as an atmosphere of nitrogen. Nylon-6 tends to form an equilibrium mixture with substantial amounts of monomer at the melt-point temperatures; therefore some corrective measure, such as removing the monomer in the melt state by evaporation, is needed. In fact, nylon-6 fibers are often washed free of monomer after spinning.

Fiber Properties

For a given denier, nylon yarn is much stronger than any other textile fiber including silk, with the exception of isotactic polypropylene. In addition to being stronger than silk, it is also lighter, having a density of only 1.14 as compared with 1.3 to 1.35 for silk. Nylon is nearly as strong when wet as when dry and does not burn, but melts. The wet and knot tenacity of nylon may be said to equal about 95 per cent of its dry tenacity. The extensibility of the wet fiber is 22 per cent as compared to 20 per cent for the dry fiber. Data are given in Tables 6.1 and 6.2.

In terms of tenacity, or tensile strength for a given weight,

TABLE 6.1. FIBER STRENGTH[2]

	Ultimate T.S. (psi)[a]	Tenacity[b] (g/denier)	Elongation[c] (%)	Density g/cc
Isotactic polypropylene	110,000	9.3	31	0.92
Polyethylene (regular)	23,000	2.0*	50 (oriented) 650 (unoriented)	0.92
Nylon (regular)	76,000	5.2	29	1.14
Nylon (high tenacity)	98,000	6.8	22	1.14
Viscose (regular)	37,000	2.0	27	1.51
Viscose (high tenacity)	73,000	3.8	18	1.51
Acetate	25,000	1.4	27	1.32
"Orlon"	66,000	4.5	16	1.15
"Dacron"	84,000	4.8	21	1.38
Glass	212,000	6.6	3	2.54
Steel	299,000	3.C	8	7.80

[a] Breaking strength of a bundle of fibers under longitudinal tension.

[b] Breaking strength of a single fiber under longitudinal tension.

[c] Extension (in the direction of load) of a fiber, caused by a tensile force, expressed as a percentage of original length.

* Estimates place value of high tenacity polyethylene at 5 to 9.

Reprinted from *Chemical Week*, 78, (24), 65 by permission of McGraw-Hill Publishing Co.

nylon ranks very high because of its strength and low specific gravity.

$$\text{Tensile strength (psi)} = \text{Tenacity (g/denier)} \times 12{,}800 \times \text{specific gravity.}$$

Based on tenacity values, the strongest fibers are nylon, saponified acetate rayon, ramie, and glass fiber. It is noteworthy that the two fibers at the top of the list in tenacity are synthetic rather than natural.

TABLE 6.2. FIBER TENACITY

	Dry (g/denier)	Wet (% of dry)
Nylon (high tenacity)	6.0-8.0	84-90
Saponified acetate ("Fortisan")	5.0-7.0	86
Ramie	6.7	130-160
Glass	6.5	92
Cotton, Sea Island	4.4-6.3	110-130
Nylon (regular)	4.5-5.7	84-90
Cotton, American, Egyptian	4.2-5.5	110-130
Silk, degummed	2.8-5.0	75-90
Cotton, American Upland	3.0-4.9	110-130
Viscose rayon (high tenacity)	3.4-4.6	61-65
Vinyl resin, Vinyon (high tenacity)	3.5-4.0	100
Viscose rayon (medium tenacity)	2.5-2.9	62
Vinyl resin, "Vinyon" (regular)	2.0-2.8	100
Vinylidene chloride	1.8-2.5	100
Viscose rayon (regular)	1.8-2.4	45-55
Cuprammonium rayon	1.7-2.3	55
Acetate rayon (regular)	1.3-1.7	60-70
Wool	1.2-1.7	80-90
Casein	0.6-0.8	40-50
Soybean protein	0.6-0.7	35-50

The natural fibers generally occupy an intermediate position with respect to tenacity, although certain grades of cotton rank quite high. Wool is far down on the list, but it has many other desirable properties, which account for its widespread use. Casein and soybean protein fibers have a lower tenacity than wool.

Toughness measures the amount of work required to rupture the fiber material. A synthetic fiber ranking high in toughness is vinylidene chloride; it is followed by nylon. Silk stands quite high in toughness and far above the other natural fibers. Glass fiber, despite is great strength, is not very tough, as the fibers are easily broken when rubbed together. See Table 6.3.

TABLE 6.3. RELATIVE TOUGHNESS OF FIBERS[19]

Fiber Material	Toughness Index
Vinylidene chloride	56
Nylon (regular)	45
Nylon (high tenacity)	41
Silk, degummed	40
Acetate, high impact	32
Silk (Tussah)	30
Vinyl resin ("Vinyon") (regular tenacity)	30
Vinyl resin ("Vinyon") (high tenacity)	25
Viscose rayon (high tenacity)	20
Wool	20
Viscose rayon (medium tenacity)	19
Saponified acetate ("Fortisan")	19
Viscose rayon (regular tenacity)	17
Acetate rayon (regular tenacity)	16
Cotton	14
Casein	14
Viscose rayon (Fiber G)	14
Cuprammonium rayon (regular tenacity)	13
Ramie	8
Abaca (Manila hemp)	7
Glass	6
Flax	6
Sisal	5
Hemp	4
Jute	2

Reprinted from the *Proceedings*, American Society For Testing Materials with the permission of the Society.

Table 6.4 gives a comparison of the stiffness of a large number of types of fibers.

TABLE 6.4. RELATIVE STIFFNESS OF FIBERS[19]

Fiber Material	Average Stiffness
Glass	290
Flax	270
Hemp	200
Jute	185
Abaca (Manila hemp)	175
Ramie	167
Sisal	127
Saponified acetate ("Fortisan")	105
Viscose rayon (Fiber G)	75
Cotton	57
Nylon (high tenacity)	41
Silk (Tussah)	24
Viscose rayon (high tenacity)	23
Nylon (regular)	22
Vinyl resin ("Vinyon") (high tenacity)	22
Vinylidene chloride	18
Silk, degummed	15
Viscose rayon (medium tenacity)	15
Cuprammonium rayon (regular tenacity)	14
Viscose rayon (regular tenacity)	10
Vinyl resin ("Vinyon") (regular tenacity)	7
Acetate rayon (regular tenacity)	5
Wool	4
Acetate, high impact	3
Casein	2

Reprinted from the *Proceedings*, American Society For Testing Materials with the permission of the Society.

When wetted with boiling water, nylon yarn will shrink to the extent of about two per cent. This fact is quite important in designing cloth structures, since full allowance must be made for shrinkage which may occur during the finish process, and careful adjusment for the lengths must be made in advance. Nylon yarn treated with steam shrinks more and more as pressure is increased. Shrinkage values of up to 14 per cent have been obtained with high pressure steam.

Moisture affinity of nylon-6,6 at different relative humidities has been found to be as follows:

	Relative Humidity (%)	Moisture Gain (%)
	10	1.4
	30	2.4
	50	3.4
	70	4.7
	90	6.7
As compared to:		
Viscose	65	11
Acetate rayon	65	5
Cotton	65	6.5

The wet tenacity of nylon is high—higher than its knot tenacity. This is a property unusual in acetate or viscose rayons. The knot tenacity varies with the type of knot as shown in Table 6.5.

TABLE 6.5. NYLON-6,6 KNOT TENACITY[9]

Type of Knot	Strength as a % of dry tenacity
Overhand	87
Figure "8"	93
Reef	Slips
Surgeon's	80
Double Surgeon's	83
Weaver's or Fisherman's	70
Weaver's (incorrectly tied)	Slips
Weaver's (correctly tied)	Slips
Double Weaver's	91
Carrick Bend	Slips
Double Carrick Bend	80
Joining Overhand	Slips
Joining Double Overhand	75
Weaver's	97

By permission of author and publishers of *Silk Journal and Rayon World*.

Mold and fungi will not grow on nylon yarn. Larva will feed on mixed fabrics, especially where wool predominates, leaving the nylon yarn untouched while the rest of the fabric is consumed. Nylon yarn has excellent resistance to alkalis and acids. However, five per cent sulfuric acid at 90°C

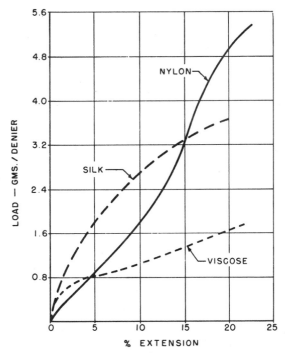

Figure 6.1. Extensibility of Fibers.
Reprinted by permission from *Silk Journal and Rayon World*

will cause five per cent loss in strength in sixteen minutes, while after six hours, there will be a loss of about 25 per cent. Stripping and scouring agents have only negligible effects on nylon.

Heating in the absence of oxygen for three hours at 200°C

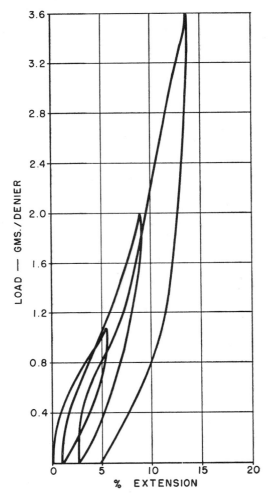

Figure 6.2. Extensibility of Nylon-6,6.
Reprinted by permission from *Silk Journal and Rayon World*

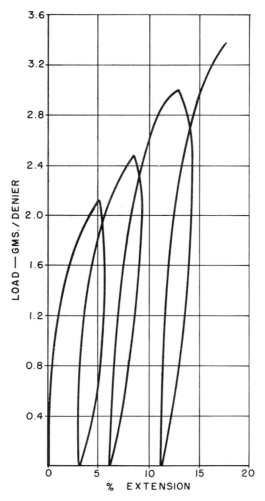

Figure 6.3. Extensibility of Silk.
Reprinted by permission from *Silk Journal and Rayon World*

or steaming at 100°C for six days do not affect nylon. It is resistant to alkali but loses 25 per cent strength in boiling water, two to three per cent in cold water, and is easily set in steam.

TABLE 6.6. FIBER COMPARISON

	Silk	Wool	Nylon
Tensile strength			
Dry, g/denier	2.8-4.7	1.0-1.5	4.5-4.8
Wet, % of dry	75-85	80-90	84-90
Elongation			
Dry, %	13-20	30-50	18-22
Wet, %	—	—	12-30

Reprinted from "Handbook of Plastics," by Simonds, Weith and Bigelow, 2nd Edition, by permission of D. Van Nostrand Co., Inc.

Stress-strain curves which illustrate the effect of time and loading on nylon, silk, or other fibers are interesting to compare.[9] The power required for recovery of nylon is superior to that of silk but, at low loadings, nylon is more extensible. See Figures 6.1, 6.2 and 6.3.

Among natural polymers it is obvious that proteins have structures similar in chemical relationship to those of synthetic polyamides. Most amide linkages in proteins are formed from α-amino acids so that the amide groups are in closer juxtaposition to each other than in synthetic polyamides.

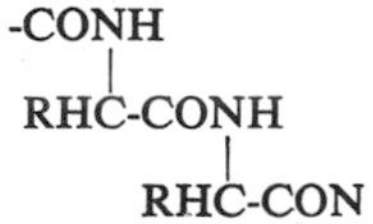

-CONH
|
RHC-CONH
|
RHC-CON

protein units

Differences between proteins depend on many other factors, including the types of R group attached to the α-amino nucleus, presence of other residues, including diaminocarboxylic acids and aminodicarboxylic acids, molecular size and shape, and spacial configurations.

It is interesting to compare some of the properties of wool and silk fibers (natural protein fibers) with those of fibers of synthetic hexamethylene adipamide (6,6-nylon).[16] See Table 6.6. In other terms, the dry tensile strength of monofils of regular nylon is in the range of 45,000 to 55,000 psi.

New Polyamide Fibers

One of the newest of the synthetic fibers is "Rilsan" polyamide made by the self polymerization of 11-aminoundecanoic acid. Like other melt spun fibers, "Rilsan" has a circular cross section. Its very low specific gravity makes it a bulky fiber. As a matter of fact, the difference in values of specific gravity make it possible to identify "Rilsan." For example, it will float in an aqueous sodium hydroxide solution of seven to eight per cent whereas nylons-6 and 6,6 will sink. Moisture absorption is also very low for "Rilsan" as compared with nylon-6 and nylon-6,6. More important, the moisture pick-up does not increase with increasing relative humidities. In this respect, "Rilsan" is somewhat like "Terylene," a polyester. "Rilsan" yarn has the following properties:

Tenacity	5 g/denier
Elongation	25%
Elastic Recovery	100% for 6% elongation

The stress and strain curve of "Rilsan" as compared with those of nylons-6 and 6,6 shows[1, 4] higher initial elastic modulus. For example, the initial elastic modulus for nylon-6 is 20 grams per denier, for nylon-6,6, 25 grams per denier and for "Rilsan" 50 grams per denier. This compares with

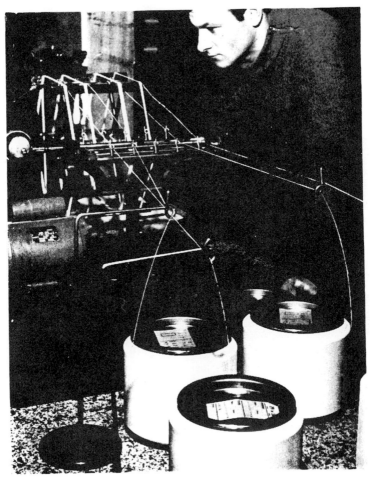

"Rilsan" Filaments
Courtesy Societe Organico

70 grams per denier for "Orlon" and 100 grams per denier for "Terylene." This higher rigidity gives better dimensional stability and suggests greater usefulness in the brush industry, where nylon-6,10 is preferred to nylon-6 and nylon-6,6 for the same reason. In the case of "Rilsan," moisture

Chair Cover Made of "Rilsan"
Courtesy Societe Organico

absorption is so low that values of tenacity and elongation are virtually identical whether the fiber is wet or dry. In other characteristics such as resistance to abrasion and bending, "Rilsan" is very similar to nylons-6 and 6,6.

The low water absorption of "Rilsan" retards penetration of dyes. Its dyeing properties are similar in other respects to those of the high molecular weight polyamides, but because of lower melting point, spun dyeing can be performed with a large selection of organic dyes. Fabrics of "Rilsan" stand up well in repeated washings with little or no yellowing. Resistance to microorganisms and to mildew is excellent, and washed fabrics dry almost instantaneously.

Fiber-Forming Considerations

Various methods for forming fibers from other kinds of polymer molecules and for drawing, crimping and other treatments have been developed. However, melt spinning of nylon is more economical than spinning of other synthetic polymers by other methods.

There are certain advantages in continuous polymerization of a nylon molecule, as with nylon-6 or "Perlon" L, and in spinning the molten polymer without first converting it into solidified chips. The economies are inherent in operating directly without cool-down, and in a continuous process which can offer a large volume output with relatively small investment in equipment. These advantages make nylon-6 a very attractive raw material for synthetic fiber production. As with most materials, there are some drawbacks, too. Nylon-6 often contains a small amount of monomeric or unreacted caprolactam which must be removed, controlled, or made use of in order to produce a successful fiber. If removed by evaporation, extraction, or other means, facilities are needed for recovering and reusing the material. Even so, it is obvious that the yield of polymer will not approach theoretical yield because of the recovery and removal of the unreacted monomer for reuse.

Dyeing of Fibers

Acetate dyestuffs are often recommended for nylon because they produce uniformity of shade even though their lightfastness is not as good as some other neutral dyeing systems. To dye nylon black, logwood, a natural dyestuff, is frequently used. Black nylon can also be obtained by using diazotized and developed acetate rayon blacks. Common wool dyestuffs have been recommended for dyeing nylon medium shades. Chrome dyestuffs can be used, but not as satisfactorily as on wool because of the difficulty of combing the dyestuff on nylon.

Polyamide fibers may be dyed with regular silk, wool and acetate colors as well as anthraquinone vat dyes, and may be waterproofed and softened by impregnating them with a two per cent solution of stearamido- or stearoxy-methylene pyridinium chloride followed by baking. Dry cleaning in the case of the common reagents presents no unusual difficulties.

During the dyeing processes, nylon fabric should be kept smooth or be "set" before dyeing. For scouring and dyeing in rope form, it is often necessary to pre-set the fabric on a roll in live steam at 10 or 15 pounds pressure to prevent the formation of permanent wrinkles. Also, it may be necessary to hold the baths at 170 to 190°F (77 to 88°C) for best results. Table 6.7 summarizes the affinities of various fibers for certain dyes.

The Chemstrand Corporation has developed and offered a new dyeing technique for nylon called "Chemnyle" which works with both filament and textured yarn, utilizing chrome dyes as well as acid and direct dyes. The process will enable sheer and tricot nylon fabrics to be color-fast when washed at 160°F and nonfading after at least 20 hours in a light-fastness accelerated test.

TABLE 6.7. AFFINITY FOR DYES OF CERTAIN FIBERS[9]

	Wool	Nylon	Acetate Rayon	Viscose Rayon
Acid wool	All	All	Very few	None
Mordant	All	All*	Some	None
Metal containing	All	All	None	None
Direct cotton	Some	Some	None	All
Dispersed (acetate rayon)	None	All	All	None
"Solacet"	All	All	All	None
Vat	All	Some*	Some	All
Azoic	Some*	Some*	Some*	All
Sulfur	Not used	Few	Not used	All
Basic	All	Some	All	All

* Special methods of application are necessary.

By permission of author and publishers of *Silk Journal and Rayon World*.

The "Chemnyle" process involves addition of certain chemicals to the dye bath at 205°C. It has been possible to produce heavy navy, black, and brown shades, in addition to other colors. Heretofore, the heavy colors have been hard to achieve with nylon fabrics. Du Pont's durable spun-dyed nylon is available only in black and the dispersed colors which are commonly used on nylon sometimes lack light-fastness and washfastness. Chemstrand has reported that 70 different dyes out of approximately 250 tested work satisfactorily in the "Chemnyle" process. The identity of the chemical additive for the dye bath has not been revealed.

Coating of Fibers[3]

Special effects are created when polyamide filaments are coated with a resin or with a rubber-like material having very different elastic properties from the nylon. By coating with rubber, curled or coiled fibers are produced and by resin coating, fibers are given a rough surface to make them wooly. To produce fibers of varying denier for special purposes, any type of filament may be drawn through the nip of two rollers rotating at equal speeds, one or both of them being provided with slots. When a thread meets a slot it is not nipped and so it is not stretched to the same extent as the rest of the thread.

Resin treatment of nylon has become more widespread since World War II. Nylon marquisettes, ordinarily used for curtains, generally have a limp feeling. To make them more lively and give a better hand, it is desirable to impart a crisp finish. Several materials are available for this purpose. Often thermoplastic resins, such as acrylates, can be used to produce a stiff feel, but the finish does not have long durability and does not have enough of the desired crispness. Melamine-formaldehyde resins, which are thermoset products, produce a crisper finish and varying degrees of stiffness can be obtained depending upon the amount of resin used. Smoothness and resilience are also imparted by use of melamine-formaldehyde resins and they are durable when handled, washed and dry cleaned. This finish also reduces yarn slippage.

Nylon taffeta too can be treated with melamine-formaldehyde resin to give different degrees of stiffness from very slight to the parchment-like finish used in petticoats. Partially polymerized urea-formaldehyde resins may also be used with taffeta but do not give quite as high a degree of resilience, smoothness or durability. Urea-formaldehyde resins can be used to treat nylon fabric for general purposes but there is a tendency for formaldehyde gas to be released on storage, especially if exposed to high humidity and high temperature.

The best finishes for the heavy-weight nylon mesh fabric used in shoe constructions are melamine-formaldehyde resins and "Permel" resin. A combination of the two will give the fabric a certain crispness which remains firm yet resilient throughout flexing. It also helps resistance to spotting by water-based substances.

Melamine-formaldehyde resins impart a crispness to unfinished, puckered nylon which is light weight and sheer but has a dead feel; they also improve the crispness of nylon lace and prevent curling.

It has been found in recent years that Raschel nettings, formerly made chiefly of cotton, can be made of lighter weight if nylon fabrics are used. Unless the nylon is treated with melamine-formaldehyde resin, however, it will tend to be soft and pliable, whereas a stiff, resilient type of structure is desirable. There is one drawback, however, to the melamine-formaldehyde finish—it increases flammability of nylon.

The Federal Flammable Act of 1954, which placed restrictions on flammability of fabrics, has made it necessary to find new finishes. Unfinished nylon fabrics have very limited flammability, ordinarily melting when exposed to a flame rather than catching fire. For example, the flame of a burning match will cause nylon fabric to burn but then melting occurs and burning ceases. This is because the heat of fusion lowers the temperature of the flame. Furthermore, the melting nylon drops away from the fabric, thus removing heat and the combustible by-product. However, the melamine finish raises the melting point of the nylon; thus instead of melting, the fabric supports combustion. The use of a thiourea-formaldehyde resin in conjunction with urea-formaldehyde resin will give nylon a stiff finish which is nonflammable. Thiourea-formaldehyde probably flame-proofs nylon by lowering the melting point, making it possible for the fabric to melt rather than burn. Although the thiourea finish reduces flammability, it does not impart as good a hand, durability, or stability as can be obtained with the melamine-formaldehyde finish. A mixture of thiourea and urea-formaldehyde resin, however, has found wide acceptance since it offers a reasonable compromise on flammability and physical appearance.

It is often necessary to size nylon yarn used for knitting or weaving to protect it and to facilitate processing. The size should be easy to remove. An aqueous solution containing partly saponified polyvinyl acetate, boric acid, and an ethylene oxide polymer typifies one of the many sizes that has been developed; the use of two to eight per cent is recommended. After the yarn has been dried and prior to knitting five per cent olive oil may be added. Butyl chloro-stearate has also been suggested as a lubricant. Nylon fibers and yarns tend to accumulate static electricity charges which can be reduced by treating them with an aqueous solution of a di-alkyl phosphonic acid.

Uses of Fibers

Nylon yarns have been used to make many kinds of textiles. While not considered a substitute for silk, it has displaced silk in the manufacture of ladies' hosiery. Many other consumer goods knitted from nylon yarn or blends of nylon yarn with other fibers have appeared on the market. These include not only full-fashioned, seamless hosiery, but half-hose and anklets, corsets, girdles, underwear, nightgowns, negligees, hostess gowns, gloves, sheer goods such as marquisette and muslin, men's hose, ties and shirts. Waterproofed nylon is used in shower curtains, umbrellas, rain coats, light tenting, and numerous other items.

In the military field, nylon fibers have been used to make parachute cloth and shroud lines for the air services. Nylon parachutes have proved useful over a wide range of conditions not only because of the great strength and elasticity of the material but also because of its mildew resistance which makes it possible to use and store it in tropical climates. For some of the same reasons the military utilize nylon for netting, screens, hammocks, ponchos, shoe laces, and electrical insulation.

Nylon is also employed in the manufacture of staple fibers as differentiated from the continuous filament type. The staple fiber, resembling wool in appearance, has been made into yarn for sweaters, swim suits, ladies' coats, and other wearing apparel.

Nylon is very often blended with wool. To such mixtures, nylon contributes a high breaking load and resistance to abrasion. The addition of five per cent staple nylon improves the spinning efficiency of wool, and only ten parts of staple nylon mixed with 90 parts of wool raises the weaving efficiency from 75 to 90 per cent.

The greatest advantage of fabrics containing nylon is the increase in the useful life of a garment made from such materials. For example, military socks, consisting of 25 per cent nylon blended with wool, have been shown to wear five times as long as all-wool socks. However, such socks are usually less comfortable since they often feel harsh and hot, and the nylon fibers tend to migrate out of the sock. Blends of the two fibers are useful in suitings and heavy-duty fabrics and garments, where there is a tendency to use lower quality wool upgraded with a small amount of nylon. Nylon staple blended with Viscose rayon also produces a satisfactory result. However, nylon-cotton blends have not been successful at all.

Tapes, webs, ply, and braided parts, including sewing thread, typewriter ribbons, sutures, fish lines, watch straps and bracelets, and parachute harnesses are made from nylon. Nylon tow ropes for gliders are advantageous inasmuch as such a rope is capable of stretching to 40 per cent of its length and of absorbing shock during glider pick-up. Nylon cord and rope are also widely accepted in military operations and as reinforcing members in tires, not only for military use but for passenger automobiles.

Nylon monofilaments of various sizes are used in super-sheer hose, corrosion resistance screens and in many bristle applications. In fact, the brush industry has been revolutionized by the introduction of the nylon bristle. They first appeared in the Dr. West's Miracle Toothbrush but are now used not only in four-fifths of all high quality toothbrushes but also in hair, clothes, nail, complexion and household-cleaning brushes. A great number of industrial brushes for bottle-labelling, cleaning, fabric printing, bottle washing, scrubbing, dry cleaning, textile fabrication, metal plating and vacuum cleaner construction are also made of nylon bristles. Tapered bristles have now displaced hog bristles for paint brushes. In sporting goods, the monofilaments are used in racket strings and for fishing leaders and lines. They are also used for furniture repair.

Many types[20] of level nylon filaments are offered for a variety of uses, as illustrated in Table 6.8. Tapered nylon filaments[20] are used chiefly in paint brushes and in brushes for industry such as floor sweeps, counter brushes, etc. They are supplied in several lengths and tapers.

Lengths	Tapers (in.)
2 in., 2¼ in.	0.009-0.006
	0.012-0.008
2½ in. to 5½ in.	0.009-0.005
in ¼ in. increments	0.012-0.008
	0.015-0.010

TABLE 6.8. NYLON FILAMENTS

Dermal Sutures ("Tynex" 2)

Property				
Elongation (%)	12-28			
Recovery (%)	40			
Melt Point (°F)	480-495			
Break Load (lb)	0.005 O.D.	1.0 lb	0.014 O.D.	7.0 lb
	0.007	2.0	0.017	10.0
	0.009	3.0	0.020	13.0
	0.011	4.5	0.023	20.0

Brush Bristles ("Tynex" 3)

Property	Uncrimped	Crimped
Tensile Strength (psi)	40,000	35,000
Stiffness (psi)	250,000	220,000
Elongation (%)	10-32	12-28
Recovery (%)	42	35
Melt Point (°F)	406-428	406-428

Fish Leader ("Tynex" 2 and 3)

Property	"Tynex" 2 (0.008-0.023 in.)	"Tynex" 3 (0.028-0.045 in.)
Elongation (%)	12-28	10-32
Recovery (%)	40	42
Melt Point (°F)	480-495	406-428
Break Load (lb)		

"Tynex" 2		0.013 O.D.	6.0 lb		
0.008 O.D.	2.5 lb	0.014	7.0	"Tynex" 3	
0.009	3.0	0.015	8.0	0.028 O.D.	30.0 lb
0.010	3.5	0.017	10.0	0.032	40.0
0.011	4.5	0.019	12.0	0.040	50.0
0.012	5.0	0.021	16.0	0.045	60.0
		0.023	20.0		

By permission of the Du Pont Company.

The bristles are not affected by alcohols other than methanol and ethanol (e.g., butanol, propanol, etc.); chlorinated solvents, such as carbon tetrachloride, chloroform, trichlorethylene; petroleum hydrocarbons, such as gasoline, benzene, naphtha, toluene, kerosene; ester solvents, such as methyl acetate, butyl acetate, isopropyl acetate, amyl acetate; aldehydes: ketones; alkalies; cleaning agents, such as soap, trisodium phosphate, trisodium phosphate-soda ash, oxalic acid.

Tire Cord

The use of nylon (generally nylon-6,6) as a reinforcement in automobile tires, to promote heat resistance, greater strength and protection against blowouts, has been growing rapidly in recent years. These tires, of extra premium grade and price, are becoming available in sizes to suit most passenger cars and many trucks. Acceptance has been most rapid where the relationship between weight of the vehicle and size of the tire results in an overload on ordinary tires.

Nylon appears to have obtained a large share of the tire yarn market, at the expense of high-tenacity rayon, and in fact may capture as much as 75 per cent (by equivalent weight) by 1960.

Late in September, 1956, Du Pont announced construction of a 40 million-pound plant to turn out nylon yarn for tire cord and other industrial products at Richmond, Virginia, near the company's present rayon yarn and cellophane plants. The plant is expected to go into operation during the latter part of 1957. Du Pont also makes heavy denier, high tenacity nylon yarn at its Seaford, Delaware, and Chattanooga, Tennessee, plants.

Chemstrand announced late in October of 1956 a new plant expansion which will raise over-all capacity to 114 million pounds annually. The expansion has progressed from an original 50 million pounds capacity to 88 million pounds scheduled for November, 1957, and 100 million pounds scheduled for January, 1958, operation, with the last stage bringing capacity to 114 million pounds by the second quarter of 1958. Chemstrand says that the added capacity, presumably the last 26 million pounds, was planned "primarily to meet the growing demand for nylon yarn in tire cord and industrial uses."[2]

Consumption of nylon in tire yarn rose from 19 million pounds in 1953 to 30 million pounds in 1954 and 50 million pounds in 1955; in 1956 it should easily top 60 million pounds. At present, there are conflicting claims regarding the extent of market saturation. Most estimates agree that the market for civilian passenger tires has hardly been touched as yet, while there are some claims that military and commercial tires have gone over completely to nylon yarn. It is estimated that roughly one-third of truck tires have been converted to nylon, with the rest likely to change over soon.

Consumption of high tenacity rayon yarn reached a peak of 430 million pounds during 1953; it declined in the following year but rose again, in 1955, to 410 million pounds used in tire yarn. The prospects for substitution of rayon with nylon to the extent of 75 per cent will eventually decrease rayon tire yarn consumption to about 150 to 200 million pounds.

One pound of nylon cord is as efficient in tire production as 1.5 pounds of rayon but, as the handling difficulties of nylon are solved, the efficiency factor is expected to rise to a one to two ratio. Of course, high tenacity rayon will inevitably improve in quality too, thus limiting advantage of nylon.

Future Prospects

Requirements for textile fibers are high molecular weight, great strength, and relatively high melting point. These products must be superpolymers having a molecular weight above 10,000. The melting point of the polymers should be no less than 200°C since textiles must withstand ironing and steaming temperatures without melting or degradation. Polyamide polymers which meet the above requirements include nylon-6,6 and 6,10, nylon-6, and polyamide-11 or "Rilsan." Although it is true that other polyamide resins having high molecular weights and melting points near 200°C have been synthesized from a variety of materials, few, if any, have attained commercial significance. Very likely other factors are involved, such as cost, difficulty of manufacture, or availability of raw material.

True synthetic fibers, unknown before 1938, are now marketed in about fifteen different varieties. Production is soaring, summary figures showing that last year synthetic fiber capacity in the United States totaled 465 million pounds.

There are many reasons for the growth of synthetics. First, the increasing demand for textiles is not met by natural fibers; second, there is a desire to create fibers which will not be at the mercy of weather, pests, and disease. Finally, the scientist is motivated to produce new and different materials, the molecular structure of which can be tailor-made to exact specifications.

The synthetic fiber field is still wide open in spite of Carother's exploratory work and the painstaking reduction of this exploration into actual successful operation. A number of new and valuable fibers have been prepared, but many more will probably be uncovered and developed in the future. Since none of the synthetic fibers is a good all-purpose fiber, we must still wait for one which can be placed on a par with natural fibers. All the synthetic fibers are strong, chemically durable and biologically resistant, but none has the capacity for absorbing moisture, a desirable trait for clothing, and none has the enormous wet extensibility of wool. The development of hydrophilic fibers would be desirable in the future.

Firmly entrenched as synthetic fibers may be, research and development work on new applications of existing fibers are continuing at a growing pace. For example, the majority of the new synthetic fibers are being used in the form of blends with natural or semi-synthetic fibers. This is now being done mechanically in textile mills.

Another significant trend in the textile industry is the increasing interest in nonwoven fabrics—structures made from textile fibers without spinning and weaving. The market in this country has grown from only a few thousand pounds eleven years ago to an estimated 50 to 75 million pounds in 1956. Consumption will probably be doubling every three years until the middle of 1960. The idea of such structures is not new. Felt, for example, is a nonwoven fabric depending on the inherent surface characteristics of wool and hair to bind the fibers together. In other nonwoven fabrics, a mass of staple is combined into a fabric either by heat or by binder adhesives.

One of the first extensive uses of nonwoven fabrics was in the manufacture of hoop skirts for teen-agers. In addition, they are being used to make apparel interlinings, filtration fabrics, aprons, dish cloths, and a variety of other items.

The future of polyamide fibers continues to look bright. The products are backed by the enormous resources of the Du Pont Company, Allied Chemical and Dye Company, Chemstrand Corporation, and several other major chemical producers. Such companies will be able to conduct the research and development necessary to keep nylon in the forefront of the synthetic fiber polymers. Nylon is still the preferred fiber for hosiery and fine textiles, and it has important uses where its high strength is definitely needed, as in military equipment, sporting goods, and sheer textiles. If prices continue on a downward path, it is very likely that production and use will increase greatly.

The prices of artificial fibers, though higher, are somewhat more stable than those of natural fibers. Although prices of natural fibers, with the exception of silk, tend to be low, they are highly variable and severe fluctuations are noted from year to year. For example, American Middling Cotton cost an average of 6.3 cents a pound in 1934; 20½ cents in 1938; 35.8 cents in 1947; 46½ cents in 1950; and 39.3 cents in 1952. The average wool price was about 13 cents per pound in 1934 to 1938; 29 cents in 1947; 52 cents in 1950; $1.52 in 1951; and 69 cents in 1952.

True synthetic fibers have properties very different from those possessed by any natural fibers, such as low moisture regain, high strength, chemical resistance and biological resistance. For this reason, the synthetics are more often complementary to, rather than competitive with, natural fibers. The one exception seems to be nylon, which has, to a great extent, displaced silk from the fiber market.

In the field of synthetic fibers, nylon is still by far the largest contributor. Production figures are as follows: in 1938, two million pounds were produced; in 1940, four million pounds; in 1945, twenty-four million pounds; in 1950, one hundred million pounds; in 1951, one hundred fifty million pounds, and in 1955 about 300 million pounds.

It is interesting to compare production of nylon fiber with that of some of the other fibers. Actual 1951 production figures are as follows: nylon, 150 million pounds; "Dacron,"

4 million pounds; "Orlon," 8 million pounds; "Dynel," 4 million pounds; "Acrylan," 1 million pounds; saran, 9 million pounds; and "Vinyon," 1 million pounds. Planned capacity for 1954 was as follows: 250 million pounds for nylon; 47 million pounds for "Dacron"; 40 million pounds for "Orlon"; 25 million pounds for "Dynel"; 30 million pounds for "Acrylan"; 20 million pounds for saran; and 2 million pounds for "Vinyon." However, all-told in 1951, the synthetic fibers accounted for less than one per cent of world fiber production and for only about five per cent of artificial fiber production. The figures are: natural fiber, 27 billion pounds; rayons, 4 billion pounds; protein fibers, 10 million pounds; and synthetic fibers, 220 million pounds. Estimated 1957 consumption in the United States of various fibers by the President's Materials Policy Commission is: cotton, 12 billion pounds; wool, 2 billion pounds; rayon, 3 billion pounds; nylon, 800 million pounds; "Orlon," 1 billion, 200 million pounds; and "Dacron," 1 billion pounds.

It appears from the above that for synthetic fibers to become more nearly competitive with natural fibers they must continually be improved and costs must be lowered.

REFERENCES

1. Aelion, R., *Fibres* (*Engineering and Chemistry*), **17**, 79 (March 1956).
2. *Chem. Week,* **78**, (24), 65 (1956).
3. Cook, T. F., and Roth, P. B., *Textile Research J.*, **26**, 229 (1956).
4. Dumon, R., *L'Industrie Texile*, **67**, 106 (1950).
5. Harris, M., "Handbook of Textile Fibers," Washington, Harris Research Laboratories, 1954.
6. Hill, R., "Fibers From Synthetic Polymers," New York, Elsevier Press, 1953.
7. Jones, C. S., *India Rubber J.*, **106**, 281 (1944).
8. Loasby, G., *Rayon Textile Monthly,* December, 1943.

9. Loasby, G., *Silk J. and Rayon World*, May, p. 32 (1943).
10. Lodge, R. M., "Fibres From Synthetic Polymers," Amsterdam, Elsevier and Co., 1953.
11. Matthews, J. M., "Matthews Textile Fibers," 6th Edition, New York, Wiley and Sons, 1947.
12. Mersereau, H. C., *Can. Chem. and Process Inds.*, **29**, 808 (1945).
13. Moncrieff, R. W., "Artificial Fibers," 2nd Edition, New York, Wiley and Sons, 1954.
14. Quig, J. B., *Textile Research J.*, **23**, 280 (1953).
15. Schildknecht, "High Polymers," Vol. 10, New York, Interscience Publishers, 1956.
16. Simonds, H. R., Weith, A., and Bigelow, M. H., "Handbook of Plastics," 2nd Edition, New York, D. Van Nostrand and Co., 1949.
17. Sherman, J. V., and Sherman, S. L., "The New Fibers," New York, D. Van Nostrand Co., 1946.
18. Soday, F. J., *Textile Research J.*, **23**, 277 (1953).
19. Smith, H. D., *Am. Soc. Testing Materials, Proc.*, **44**, 543 (1944).
20. "Tynex" Nylon Bulletin, E. I. du Pont de Nemours and Co., Inc.

7. MOLDING, CASTING AND EXTRUSION

Thermoplastic polyamide resins are molded under heat and pressure; reactive amino-containing polyamide resins can be cast into molded forms as thermoset reaction products. Both types of applications will be covered in this chapter. The basic chemistry of the materials is described in Chapter 3.

Present Consumption Patterns

Polyamide resin molding material showed increased usage in 1954, but progress has been slow because most moldings are small parts that must be specially engineered. It is believed that about 12 million pounds were used for molding in 1953 and probably 15 million pounds in 1954.

Although nylon is one of the most expensive of the thermoplastics, its low specific gravity makes it competitive with many metals. (Table 7.1) At a price of about $1.60 per pound for nylon-6,6, a cubic foot is worth about $110, compared with about $18 for phenolics, $21 for polystyrene and $36 for cellulose acetate.

Nylon molding compounds are marketed by a number of manufacturers, but not many use more than two or three

TABLE 7.1. DENSITY OF NYLON AND OTHER BEARING MATERIALS

Material	Density lbs/cu ft
Nylon	71
Aluminum	169
Wood's Metal	605
Copper	530
Bronze	548
Brass	535
Zinc	417
Cast Iron	455
Stainless Steel	485
Babbitt	462
Powdered Iron	471
Powdered Copper	530
Powdered Bronze	548

tons of nylon per month. The types of products offered for sale in the United States[16] are listed in Table 7.2.

Nylon moldings are used for small bearings, bushings, valve bodies, and other wearing surfaces, especially where heat resistance, toughness, and low friction qualities are needed. See Table 7.3.

Until recently, few items have been made requiring more than several ounces of nylon. There is no nylon molding end-use application which commands a multimillion-pound market. The automotive companies use about one-half to three-fourths pound per car (particularly General Motors and Ford), in a number of applications including domelight covers, door catches, speedometer gears and small bearings.

TABLE 7.2. NYLON MOLDING RESINS MARKETED IN THE UNITED STATES

Trade Name	Manufacturer	Sales Agent	Types	Grades
Zytel	Polychemicals Dept., E. I. du Pont de Nemours & Co., Inc.	Polychemicals Dept., E. I. du Pont de Nemours & Co., Inc.	Nylon-6,6 and 6,10	11
Plaskon	National Aniline Div., Allied Chemical & Dye Corp.	Barrett Div., Allied Chemical & Dye Corp.	Nylon-6	2
Spencer Nylon	Spencer Chemical Co.	Spencer Chemical Co.	Nylon-6	8
Durethan	Farbenfabriken Bayer AG Leverkusen, Germany	Hercules Powder Co.	Nylon-6	1
Grilon	Holzverzuckerungs AG Zurich 1, Switzerland	Alfred C. Toepfer, 1 Broadway, N.Y. 4, N.Y.	Nylon-6	6
Ultramid	Badische Aniline & Soda-Fabrik AG Ludwigshafen, Germany	Nova Chemical Corp., 147-153 Waverly Place, N.Y. 14, N.Y.	Nylon-6 and 6,6	3

Reprinted from *Modern Plastics* by permission of Breskin Publications, Inc.

TABLE 7.3. UNITED STATES CONSUMPTION OF NYLON
MOLDING POWDER BY INDUSTRY* (x 1000 lbs.)

	1950	1951	1952	1953	1954	1955
Automotive	350	940	1,670	252	3,380	3,940
Electrical	90	220	350	550	750	730
Gears, bearings, and bushings	1,050	1,800	3,380	4,950	6,300	6,600
Medical	430	400	700	980	1,000	1,500
Textile	90	220	350	550	620	2,100
Other	90	220	350	550	750	730
Total	2,100	3,800	6,800	10,100	12,800	15,600

* The figures exclude resin used for wire coatings in the Korean War as this use is not part of the stable growth market, but represents only a temporary demand.

Reprinted from *Modern Plastics* by permission of Breskin Publications, Inc.

Many of these parts may be produced at the rate of several per pound, and in some instances at the rate of over 100 per pound.

Outstanding Properties

Of the types of nylon used for molding in the United States, nylon-6,6 and nylon-6 have so far assumed the greatest importance. Some of their characteristics are compared below.

Characteristics	Nylon-6	Nylon-6,6
Hardness	Lesser	Greater
Impact strength	Greater	Lesser
Melting point	Lower	Higher
Melt viscosity	Higher	Lower
Molding cycle	Longer	Shorter
Abrasion resistance	Lesser	Greater
Moldability	Better	Poorer
Brittleness	Lower	Greater
Flexibility	Greater	Lesser
Shrinkage	Less	More
Heat resistance	Lower	Higher

The most important application of nylon is as an engineering material—in bearings, gears, cams and other mechanical parts. It is especially suited for such use because of its outstanding properties.

Baby carriages roll smoothly and quietly with wheel bearings of nylon resin which require no lubrication. This is one of the first nylon bearing applications to go into commercial production, although the material is now widely used for bearings, gears, and other mechanical parts.
Courtesy Du Pont Co.

Thermal Resistance. Nylon has considerably better heat resistance than any other thermoplastic material, and will withstand continued exposure to temperatures tolerated by many of the thermosetting plastics. Nylon-6,6 has a melting temperature of 507°F, and a heat-distortion temperature, under 66 psi loading, of 405°F. Nylon bearings have been known to perform satisfactorily at surface temperatures above 300°F where lubrication was adequate. Nylon is, however, more sensitive to dry heat than to moist heat. Continuous exposure to dry heat in excess of 250°F may cause embrittlement of the material.

Nylon Chair Glides resist impact and abrasion. They present a hard, self-lubricating surface and slide easily over floor.
Courtesy Barrett Division, Allied Chemical and Dye

Chemical Resistance. Nylon-6,6 is insoluble in common organic solvents and inert to alkalies. Dilute mineral acids and most organic acids can often be tolerated, even though the resistance to acids is not outstanding. Petroleum oils and greases do not affect nylon at temperatures as high as 325°F, nor are oils and greases affected by nylon, as demonstrated

TABLE 7.4. PROPERTIES OF MOLDED NYLON

Property	Method	Nylon-6,6	Nylon-6,10
MECHANICAL PROPERTIES			
T.S. (psi) 70°F	D638-44T	15,700	12,900
77°F	D638-44T	10,900	7,000
170°F	D638-44T	7,600	6,760
Elong. (%) 70°F	D638-44T	1.6	2.0
77°F	D638-44T	50	135
170°F	D638-44T	320	320
Modulus of Elasticity (psi) 77°F	D638-44T	400,000	260,000
Shear Str (psi)	D732-43T	9,600	8,400
Impact Str, Izod, ft-lb, 40°F	D256-43T	0.4	1.6
77°F	D256-43T	1.5	2.7
Stiffness (psi) 77°F	D747-46T	300,000	150,000
Flexual Str (psi) 77°F	D790-442	14,600	9,500
Compressive Stress at 1% Deformation (psi)	D695-44T	4,900	3,000
Creep in Flexure	Arl P-25	90	120
Hardness, Rockwell	D785-47T	R118	R111
THERMAL PROPERTIES			
Flow Temperature, °F	D569-44T	480	397
Coefficient of Linear Thermal Exp, per °F	D696-44T	5.5×10^{-5}	8.2×10^{-5}
Thermal conductivity, Btu/hr/sq ft/°F/in.	Arl P-32	1.7	1.5
Specific Heat		0.4	0.4
Deformation under load, %, 122°F, 2000 psi	D621-44T	1.4	4.2
Heat-distortion temp. °F:		170°F	130°F
264 psi	D648-45T		
66 psi	D648-45T	400°F	320°F

TABLE 7.4. PROPERTIES OF MOLDED NYLON (Continued)

Property	Method	Nylon-6,6	Nylon-6,10
ELECTRICAL PROPERTIES			
Dielectric strength, v/mil:			
Short time	D149-44	385	470
Step by step	D149-44	340	410
Volume resistivity, ohm-cm	D257-45	4.5×10^{13}	4×10^{14}
Dielectric constant, 60 cycles	D150-45T	4.1	4.6
10^3 cycles	D150-45T	4.0	4.5
10^6 cycles	D150-45T	3.4	3.5
Power factor, 60 cycles	D150-45T	0.014	0.04
10^3 cycles	D150-45T	0.02	0.04
10^6 cycles	D150-45T	0.04	0.03
OTHER PROPERTIES			
Water-Absorption, %	D570-42	1.5	0.04
Flammability	D635-44	Self-extin-guishing	Self-extin-guishing
Specific Gravity	D792-44T	1.14	1.09
Mold Shrinkage, in./in.		0.015	0.015
Compression Ratio	D392-38	2.1	2.2

Tests have been performed by ASTM methods unless otherwise indicated. The prefix Arl refers to test methods used in the Du Pont Arlington laboratories.

(1) Term "creep in flexure" is a measure of the deformation under a prolonged standard load. Results here represent mils deflection in 24 hours of a ⅛-in. by ½-in. bar, 4-in. span, center load flatwise to 1000 psi, minus the initial deflection.

(2) Thermal conductivity measured by Cenco-Fitch apparatus.

(3) Samples measured ⅛-in. thick under dielectric strength.

by the Underwood test of SAE. Food acids, lactic acid milk, photographic solutions and the like, have little or no effect on nylon moldings. The chemical inertness of nylon permits its use in direct contact with a wide variety of chemical solutions, and this often contributes to simplicity of machine design by avoiding the necessity for fluid seals. Frequently the fluid being handled can be allowed to enter the bearing to serve as an effective lubricant and coolant.

Abrasion Resistance. The abrasion resistance of nylon is outstanding among unfilled plastics. Nylon yields slightly at the surface but shows little wear over extended periods of service in thermally stable installations. Its load-carrying ability and temperature range are approximately those of babbitt, with considerably better abrasion resistance. Both gears and sleeve bearings of nylon tested in the presence of abrasive materials, such as sand, have outworn metal components by far, under the same test conditions.

Other Properties. Nylon is also noted for its great impact strength, high strength even in thin sections, lightness, ability to reduce noise, and ease of lubrication.[4] (See Table 7.4.)

Molded Machine Parts

Nylon bearings, gears, grommets and fasteners are becoming standard in many fields, since nylon can do a better job than many other materials. It requires little or no lubrication and can be easily kept clean. However, the bearings must be designed to permit shrinkage and expansion with changing humidity conditions in the atmosphere. For example, although nylon-6,6 has excellent physical properties, it is difficult to mold due to its highly erratic shrinkage characteristics. Gears must be designed from nylon with looser tolerances than those where metal is used. There is a trend toward the use of nylon not only as a replacement for metal pieces, but for development of new parts. To gain full usefulness, however, nylon requires careful handling.

In evaluating nylon as a bearing material, interesting comparisons have been made on wear studies of nylon to nylon,

nylon to brass and nylon to steel, all under various loads and speeds and with different lubricants. The lowest rates of wear occur when nylon is run against nylon in a dry condition and against steel lubricated with SAE 10 oil. When nylon is rubbed against brass, metal flakes off and contaminates the bearings.

Cutaway view of sensing unit for explosion and fire suppression device, used primarily in jet aircraft fuel tanks. The rise in pressure caused by the incipient stage of an explosion compresses the bellows fabricated of nylon resin. This action closes the circuit which actuates a mechanism for spreading a mist of suppressant in the explosion area and dampening the ignited vapors—all within a few milliseconds.
Courtesy Du Pont Co.

Quite a range of machine parts and structural items are now being made of nylon. These include not only gears and bearings but also such parts as connecting rods in electric shavers, counting dials, cams and ratchets on calculating machines, continuous belts, light bulb housings, drain hose elbows, coil form pulleys, screws, valve seats, washers, pump impellers and hydraulic needles. Some of the parts used on linotype machines made of nylon include gears for rubber keyboard rolls, assembly stars, matrix buffers, control knobs, pulleys and sprockets, and stop sleeves.

Nylon gears are used for polishing machines where smooth, quiet operation and minimum maintenance are requirements.[9] The Maytag Washing Machine Company uses nylon parts for bearings in washing machines, and most refrigerators now have nylon doorlatch rollers and valve parts for aerosol containers made of nylon. It is also used for molded pinion gears for out-board motor starters. Nylon goes into dozens of parts for coin boxes on busses (made by the Grant Money Meters Company), conveyors belts and rewinders for wire threads.[9] Such widely different items as windshield-wiper motors, tubeless tire puncture sealers, fishing reels, hardware for the building industry, silverware racks, fasteners and rivets are typical of the many parts which are now being molded from nylon.

Other molded nylon parts include timing gears, speedometer gears, small bearings and bushings for automotive parts, coil forms, battery cases, gears for kitchen equipment, utensil handles, electric shaver parts, gears, bearings and cams for office equipment, combs, brush backs, hammer facings and camera parts.

The use of nylon in these and other parts demonstrates its wide range of application, which is now being developed to an even greater extent.

Molded nylon is used in many textile machinery parts, thereby eliminating a particularly troublesome problem in this industry. Nylon bearings on the take-up rolls of yarn-twisting machinery run without oil, and show no wear even

Carrying over a quarter-million cans of beer per eight-hour shift, this flat top conveyer chain made entirely of nylon resin is providing economies in brewing operations ("Nylite" chain manufactured by Fenco, Inc., 125 N. Racine Ave., Chicago 7, Ill. Parts of "Zytel" molded by Du Bois Plastic Products Co., 170 Florida St., Buffalo, New York.)
Courtesy Du Pont Co.

after years of continuous use. As a result, the yarn being handled remains free from spattered oil or metal particles from worn bearings. Other uses in textile machinery include thread guides of many types and parts for drafting equipment, spinning equipment, looms and winding machines.

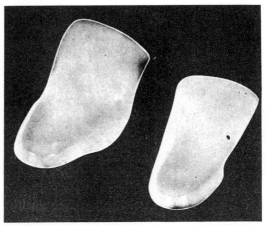

Inner Soles of Nylon, are designed for use with golf shoes. Nylon is ideal for this application because it easily supports golfer's weight and because cleats may be screwed into it.
Barrett Division, Allied Chemical and Dye

Such electrical parts as fuse holders and insulating bushings are made of nylon, for its combination of insulating properties with mechanical strength and heat resistance.

A number of automobiles have lenses made of nylon in overhead and other interior lamps. The material's toughness and ability to be molded in very thin sections enable lenses only 0.025 inch thick to withstand rough treatment in both assembly and service. Their flexibility permits them to be snapped into place easily, without the use of gaskets required for lenses made of more rigid materials.

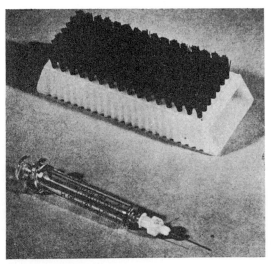

Medical items molded of nylon resin, such as this hypodermic needle hub and surgeon's scrub brush, withstand repeated sterilizations in the steam autoclave.
Courtesy Du Pont Co.

Because of its toughness, physiological inertness, and ability to withstand repeated sterilization in a steam autoclave, nylon is used in a number of medical applications, including hypodermic needle parts, parts for blood-transfusion kits, respiratory valves, and surgeon's scrub brushes.

Molding of Nylon

Nylon-6,6 can be molded in conventional injection machines[4] or in an injection cylinder having a correctly designed nozzle and proper distribution of heat. In general, diverging-type cylinders and vertical cylinders can be heated to a higher over-all temperature than horizontal straight-bore cylinders.

The injection ram may be cored to permit cooling in machines having close clearance between the cylinder wall and ram. Nylon should generally be injected into the mold at high speed.

A technician removes combs made of nylon resins from a modern injection machine at the Polychemicals Sales Service Laboratory. The Du Pont laboratory is located at Chestnut Run near Wilmington, Delaware.
Courtesy Du Pont Co.

The conventional straight-bore nozzle, without a reverse taper, is not recommended for molding nylon.[4] A nozzle of this design must be operated at temperatures over 700°F to prevent freeze-off between shots. At such temperatures drooling cannot be controlled, and the molded articles tend to have a rough, splay-marked surface. A reverse taper nozzle is preferred.

Although molten nylon is more fluid than other thermoplastics, it will solidify almost at the instant of contact with the relatively cold mold surface, thus eliminating any undue tendency to flash. When flashing occurs, the line pressure should be reduced, but the high rate of injection should be maintained.

When close tolerances are required, however, the following is recommended:[4]

1. Using the specified dimensions, machine a single cavity in the mold-base intended for use in production.
2. Machine the sprue bushing and all runners up to the positions where the production cavities will be inserted. This will establish the time required for the material to reach the cavities.
3. By trial moldings in the single cavity, determine optimum runner and gate size (as described below), and determine the molding conditions that are necessary to produce satisfactory molded parts.
4. Heat-treat the molded part for one-half hour at 350°F, and allow to cool slowly.
5. Check the dimensions of the treated article after at least 24 hours. Note changes in any dimension.
6. Use shrinkage data thus obtained to adjust the dimensions of the production mold.
7. Machine production cavities to the correct dimensions, and insert them into the production mold base that was used for the single-cavity test molding.
8. Mold under the conditions previously established, without altering the runners. Compensation for slight differences in dimensions can be readily made by altering molding conditions slightly.

A moisture content over 0.28 per cent in the molding powder will reduce the toughness of molded or extruded products. Nylon molding powders readily absorb atmospheric moisture. The rate of absorption is accelerated when relative humidity is high and when a comparatively large surface area of powder is exposed, for example, when it is spread thinly in unheated trays. Too much moisture in the granular nylon being molded will cause excessive drooling at the nozzle and poor control of dimensions, in addition to reduced toughness.[4]

Nylon-6,6 can be molded at cylinder temperatures of 520 to 720°F. The choice of temperature will be based primarily on the quantity of material to be melted, the cross-section of the article being molded, and the design of the cylinder.

In many cases, the use of higher molding temperatures (600 to 700°F) improves the properties of the molded piece. In general, however, the temperature of the mold should be about 100°F; temperatures above 150°F are seldom necessary.

Normal injecting pressure should range between 10,000 and 18,000 psi. If the sprue and gates are too small, the pressure required to inject may have to be increased to 20,000 psi.[4]

The length of cycle should be one minute per one-quarter inch of thickness.

The variables of the molded article (size, shape, etc.) affect shrinkage and the magnitude of the stresses set up in the item. Stresses may relieve themselves in time, depending on the conditions to which the article is exposed, but the time required is unpredictable. To insure against dimensional change caused by relief of such stresses, it is important that residual stresses be relieved by heat treating soon after molding.

The temperature of the heat-treating liquid should be well above the temperature to which the article will be exposed in use—preferably about 350°F, and not over 400°F.

Extrusion of Nylon

A typical extruder[4] for nylon resin is shown in Figure 7.1. The major features of the extruder are as follows:

1. Electrically heated barrel.
2. Metering-type screw.
3. Screen and breaker plate.

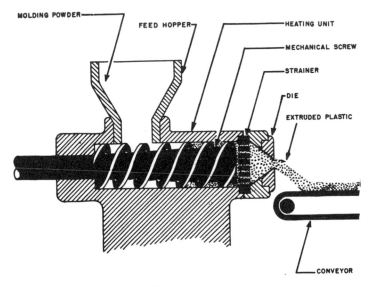

Figure 7.1. Extrusion Head.
Courtesy Du Pont Company

Comparatively long barrels are desirable in order to introduce the great **amount of heat** required without having to use temperatures close to the decomposition point of the resin. The ratio of the length of the barrel to its diameter should be at least 12 to 1.

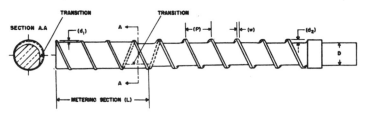

Figure 7.2. Extrusion Screw.
Courtesy Du Pont Company

The type of screw shown in Figure 7.2 works best.[4] It is characterized by flights of constant depth and constant pitch at the feed section of the screw. The last three flights have a shallow, constant depth. This section, called the metering section of the screw, pumps the material at a uniform rate, and generates sufficient pressure to force it through the die. The compression from the feed to the metering section occurs abruptly and usually takes place over one-quarter turn as an involute compression.

The following design is suggested for a screw to be used in the extrusion of nylon.

Type = metering, sudden compression
Pitch = diameter × 1.0 (constant)
Length of metering section = 4 flights
Depth of channel at metering section = diameter × 0.04
Depth of channel at feed section = diameter × 0.05
Width of land = diameter × 0.1
Compression ratio = 4 to 1.

As in the case of injection molding, it is important that the molding powder be dried before extrusion.[4]

Cross-head and die assemblies for coating wire with nylon have been carefully developed. Vacuum is applied between the wire and guider tip in order to pull the flowing cone of plastic close to the die. In this way, a smoother coating is achieved, and adhesion may be improved. The annular space between the guider tip and the die, at the point where the molten nylon is extruded upon the wire, should have a thickness of between five and eight times the desired thickness of the coating on the wire. The wire passes through the head faster than the molten resin is fed upon it, and the thickness of the layer of resin is reduced as it is being deposited on the wire. Thus the thickness of the coating is controlled by correlating the speed of the extruder and the take-off speed of the wire. Between the quench bath and take-off, the wire may be spark-tested for breaks in the insulation.

Tubing is also produced by extrusion. Because of the fluidity of most nylons in the molten state, air pressure inside the tube must approximate that on the outside to avoid deformation of the tube. Air under regulated pressure is introduced into the tubing through an open-end "T." This makes possible the production of a small variety of sizes and wall thicknesses with a single die.

All commercial types of nylon molding powder can be extruded as sheeting. The stiffness and transparency of nylon sheeting are affected by chilling rate. Cold water tends to make the film more transparent and flexible, while hot water makes it more opaque and stiff. This sensitivity to temperature of the quench water necessitates that the bath have good circulation to prevent the development of localized areas of hot water that will cause streaks and spots on the sheet. At the same time, however, this circulation must not cause impingement of streams of water on the uncooled sheet.

The sheet is pulled by a pair of driven rubber rolls. The rate at which these rolls are turning with respect to the rate at which the sheet is extruded will control the caliper.

Bearing Tests

Various lubricants have been tried in bearing tests with nylon, including water and SAE 10 motor oil at a temperature of 125°F, and SAE 30 motor oil at room temperature.[17]

Rate of wear is initially high but rapidly decreases as the surface becomes polished. The coefficient of friction becomes less as running continues, up to about four hours. After this period, it usually remains constant. The rate of wear appears to become minimum after about 0.001 to 0.002 inches have been removed from the surface of the nylon. From tests against steel and brass, it appears probable that this amount of nylon must be removed to smooth the steel or brass enough so that it does not wear the nylon specimen further. This condition applies mainly to machined, unpolished surfaces, and is not so evident when molded bushings having a polished surface are run against a smooth shaft.[17]

During the tests with water lubrication, wear rates increase when wear debris, suspended in the water, is allowed to remain in the bearing during the test period. Hence, it is recommended that, when water is used as a lubricant, there be sufficient flow of water through the bearing to assure removal of wear debris as formed.

Combinations of nylon and nylon generally give the lowest rate of wear and lowest coefficient of friction; nylon and steel are almost as good; and nylon and brass are the poorest. Where corrosion is a problem, it is recommended that stainless steel be employed rather than brass or bronze.

In the Neely machine, since the specimen is in contact with the wear plate for only 10 per cent of the cycle, frictional heat does not become a factor in the test.[17]

In actual sleeve bearing tests using various shaft materials, steel appeared to be the best. Nylon bearings against shafts of cold-drawn steel support loads as high as 206 psi, the load limit of the test equipment for a 1¼-in. diameter bearing at a rubbing velocity of 525 fpm.

Upper limits of loads and speeds for nylon bearings can be extended by providing for the dissipation of frictional heat, either by the use of ample lubrication or by the design of the bearing and mounting. Exceptionally long service life may be expected from a bearing or gear installation where the temperatures of the contact surface are stabilized well below the heat distortion point. Surface temperatures up to 250°F are satisfactory. Temperatures above 300°F are successfully tolerated where loading is not excessive.

Thin-section nylon moldings are more dimensionally stable than thicker sections, and are less affected by changes of moisture content and temperature. This greater dimensional stability permits better control of operating clearances. A thick bearing wall introduces excessive thermal insulation between the bearing face and the mounting structure, thus retarding the dissipation of frictional heat.

Water is a satisfactory lubricant for nylon but not as good as a high-grade motor oil. When, however, it is desirable or necessary to employ water as a lubricant, this loss of bearing efficiency must be justified on the basis of the imposed conditions. The same reasoning applies to the use of unlubricated bearings and bearings running in milk, gasoline, solvents or other unorthodox lubricants. The use of ineffective lubricants has an adverse effect on the service life or capacity of a bearing; this is much less in the case of nylon than it is with other materials.

The initial break-in period of unlubricated bearings is very critical if they are run at or near maximum capacity. Their service life can be appreciably extended by applying light oil or grease at the time of installation to protect them during the first few hours of operation.[17] Data are given in Tables 7.5 and 7.6.

TABLE 7.5. RESULTS OF RATES OF WEAR TESTS

Rubbing Agents	Load (psi)	Lubricant	Rubbing Speed (fpm)	Wear (mil)	Aver. Friction Coefficient
Nylon vs Nylon	1050	None	156	1.6	0.039-0.099
Nylon vs Cold Drawn Steel	1050	Water	156	9.0	0.494
Nylon vs Cold Drawn Steel	1050	SAE No. 10 Oil	156	0.9	0.140

Reprinted from *Product Engineering*, 21 (7), 102 (1950) by permission of McGraw-Hill Publishing Co.

TABLE 7.6. EFFECT OF LUBRICANT ON LIMITING LOADS DURING RUBBING TESTS

Rubbing Agents	Limiting Loads (psi)	Lubricant
Nylon vs Steel	1550	Oil
Nylon vs Steel	1050	Water
Nylon vs Steel	550	No lubrication

NOTES: Data obtained from Bulletin No. 21 — E. I. du Pont de Nemours & Co., Inc.

(1) Data for the "breaking-in periods." After this period rate of wear becomes negligible.

(2) Tests do not indicate effect of frictional heat.

Reprinted from *Product Engineering*, 21 (7), 102 (1950) by permission of McGraw-Hill Publishing Co.

Rate of wear is generally greatest at the start but it tapers off with further operation. Perhaps this is because, after the surface of the nylon is glazed and a more intimate contact is established, there results a decrease in unit pressure. In gear designs where speeds or loads may be excessive, the low heat conductivity of nylon, which is 1.7 Btu's per hour per square foot per °F per inch, must be considered. Experimental gears have been made with copper shims to facilitate conducting heat away from the gear tooth area.

The horse-power transmitting capacity of a nylon gear can be determined by the formula:

$$HP = \frac{9.5 \times 10^{-5} \times SWS \times FW \times Y \times PLV}{DP}$$

where *SWS* equals safe working stress, *FW* width of face in inches, *Y* the tooth factor, *PLV* the pitch line velocity, and *DP* diametrical pitch in inches. See Table 7.7.

TABLE 7.7. SAFE WORKING STRESS OF NYLON AT INDICATED PITCH LINE VELOCITIES

Ply (ft per min.)	Nylon-6,6
100	4500
150	4071
200	3750
250	3500
400	3000
500	2786
800	2400
1000	2250
1500	2029
2000	1909
2500	1833
3000	1781
4000	1715

Reprinted from *Product Engineering*, 21 (7), 102 (1950) by permission of McGraw-Hill Publishing Co.

Nylon can damp mechanical vibrations, thus reducing noise. This property is being utilized in many mechanical items for home and industrial use and in sound recording and motion picture equipment. The conformability of nylon and its ability to deform slightly to absorb shock make it desirable for use on gears and where impact loading is encountered. This same property of conformability enables nylon gears to mesh satisfactorily with metal gears and to iron out any irregularity that may be apparent on the gear faces.

A. J. Cheney, Jr., W. B. Happoldt, and K. G. Swayne have described the use of nylon materials as bearings.[2]

TABLE 7.8. BOILING TIMES FOR MOISTURE CONDITIONING OF NYLON-6,6

Wall Thickness (in.)	Boiling Time (hr)
Average air exposure:	
0.060	0.5
0.090	1.2
0.125	6
0.250	18
Wet applications:	
0.060	4
0.090	10
0.125	50
0.250	180

Reprinted from the April and May, 1956, issues of *Plastics Technology* by permission of the publishers.

Nylon-6,6 resin, available as Du Pont's "Zytel" 101, should be stress-relieved at a temperature of near 50°F higher than the maximum expected. This can be done by heat treating in a suitable oil or other liquid.

The coefficient of thermal expansion of nylon is a very important factor since it is several times as large as that of metals often used in bearing applications. Another factor is the hygroscopic character of nylon, previously mentioned; it absorbs moisture until a state of equilibrium is reached. Here again, nylon is subject to dimensional change. Thus, it is important to condition bearings to moisture near equilibrium and to maintain temperature control. One simple treatment is to boil the nylon bearings until approximately 3 per cent by weight of water has been absorbed (Table

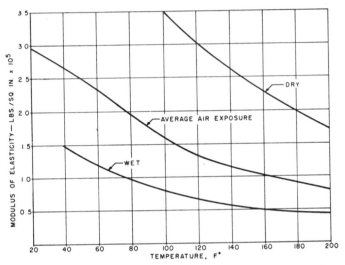

Figure 7.3. Effect of Environment on Modulus of Nylon-6,6.
Courtesy Plastics Technology April, May, 1956

7.8). If parts are left standing in air for a period of time excess surface moisture will evaporate; thus, most dimensional changes will have taken place by the time the bearing is to be used. Strength and the stiffness also depend upon moisture content. Nylon parts *must* be sized so that the desired dimensions will be obtained once they are at equilibrium with surface conditions, including both temperature

TABLE 7.9. MOISTURE ABSORPTION AND DIMENSIONAL CHANGE
OF NYLON-6,6 MOLDED BEARINGS

Environment	Moisture Content (% by wt)	Change of Inside Diameter (in./in. of diam.)
As molded	Less than 0.3	—
Average air exposure	2.5	+ 0.006
In water	8.5	+ 0.025

Reprinted from the April and May, 1956, issues of *Plastics Technology* by permission of the publishers.

TABLE 7.10. WATER ABSORPTION BY POLYAMIDES

Polyamide Trade Name	Weight Increase		
	14 Days %	Immersion in Water at Room Temperature Maximum Value %	Immersion for 3 hr in Boiling Water %
Ultramide A	10.0	10.0	8.5
Ultramide B	6.8	10.9	3.3
Ultramide B special	9.3	9.8	7.6
Ultramide 6A	12.2	14.0	16.3
Nylon-6,6 or nylon FM-10001	10.2	10.2	8.6
Nylon FM-3001	3.2	3.2	3.7
Nylon FM-6401	9.6	10.7	Destroyed
Akulon M 2	10.6	11.6	8.3
Rilsan	1.6	2.2	2.4
Polyurethane U	2.1	2.2	2.4
Nylon AF	8.6	8.9	7.3
Grilon	10.0	11.2	6.8

Reprinted from "Die Polyamide," by Hopff, Muller, and Wenger, by permission of Springer-Verlag.

and humidity. Through annealing and moisture conditioning, inside dimensions can be held to a plus or a minus one mil. The effects of moisture on dimensions are shown in Table 7.9 while data on moisture absorption for various poly-amides[6] are shown in Table 7.10.

The stiffness or deformation under capacity load can be calculated from the modulus of elasticity.[2] Since the modulus can vary with temperature and moisture content, as shown in Figure 7.3, one must calculate the stiffness under the conditions to be used.

"Creep" or cold flow should also be considered. A part under compressive stress will deform with time. One way to look at this phenomenon is to consider it as continued change in modulus with time. From comparative measurements of changing modulus, it is possible to calculate deformation with time, or in other words "creep."

TABLE 7.11. COEFFICIENTS OF FRICTION FOR NYLON-6,6

Lubricant	Nylon on Nylon		Steel on Nylon	
	Static	Kinetic	Static	Kinetic
Dry	0.46	0.37	0.37	0.34
Water	0.52	0.33	0.23	0.19
Ethylene glycol	0.58	0.19	0.20	0.16
Glycerol	0.36	0.19	0.23	0.18
Perfluorolube oil	0.58	0.24	0.30	0.19
Oleic acid	0.29	0.13	0.15	0.08
Polymethyl siloxane (DC 500)	0.43	0.17	0.19	0.12

Reprinted from the April and May, 1956, issues of *Plastics Technology* by permission of the publishers.

Data in Table 7.11 for coefficient of friction for Nylon 6,6 were obtained with a modified Bowden-Leben stick slip machine. The performance of nylon in the presence of lubricants is surprisingly good. High loads at medium to high speeds are supported even though little lubricant is present.

Polyamide-11

"Rilsan," or polyamide-11, is supplied as a molding powder of low density (1.04). Though its moisture absorption is lower than for many other polyamides, the powder should be dried for a few hours at 80°C before molding.[13]

Injection pressure for molding is usually in the order of 300 to 700 kg/cm². "Rilsan" will shrink 1 to 1.5 per cent. Articles molded of "Rilsan" will absorb 0.5 to 1.1 per cent of moisture in saturated atmospheres.

The various grades of "Rilsan" for molding are:

"Rilsan" B.M.O.—standard quality, rigid and translucent
B.M.2—ivory white modification of B.M.O.
B.M.O.P20—translucent, flexible grade
B.M.2P20—ivory white and flexible
G.8.—graphited B.M.O.

Various colors can be obtained.

The mechanical properties of polyamide-11—its toughness, elongation, resistance to compression, flexing strength and abrasion resistance—are excellent. When oriented, as in a fiber, it has unusually high strength. But even in the unoriented state, such as in molded plastics or electrical cable coverings, its toughness is in the order of 9,000 to 10,000 psi and its maximum elongation is between 60 and 250 per cent. Compressive yield strength ranges from 12,000 to 16,000 psi and, even at low temperatures, the impact resistance is very good. The coefficient of friction is from

0.11 to 0.18 on dry steel surfaces. It offers a hard and highly polished surfacing material.[13]

"Rilsan," like other polyamides, has excellent resistance to alkalis, oils, hydrocarbons and many other chemicals. Cresol is one of the few good solvents.

Molded Gears of "Rilsan"
Courtesy Societe Organico

"Rilsan" may be injection-molded on modern presses.[13] Since its melting point is near 186°C and its decomposition point around 265°C, a wide range of molding temperatures may be selected. However, molding should be conducted above the melting point but not far above 240°C to avoid oxidation and needless lowering of viscosity. The hard

"Rilsan" B.M.O. is used for manufacture of parts for electrical insulation. Complicated shapes of molds may be selected and low or thin-walled thicknesses may be made. Walls as thin as 0.016 inch are not uncommon. "Rilsan" is used for making terminal supports, insulating prongs, screws, nuts and bolts for radio assemblies. It is also made into jacks and framework for coils for the telephone field. For household use, discs and insulated housings, which resist overheating and are nearly unbreakable, are made of "Rilsan."

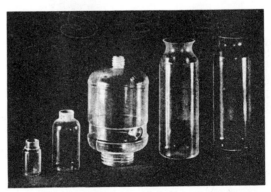

Bottles and Flasks Formed from "Rilsan" Polyamide-11
Photograph By Prisma-Photo
Courtesy Societe Organico

In France, windshields and blinkers, coilheads, wall plugs, and insulating apparatus for aircraft have been made of "Rilsan."

"Rilsan" can be extruded on conventional equipment without difficulty, providing that the material has been dried and that extrusion temperatures of 200°F or higher are used. On leaving the die, the extruded material must be cooled quickly to avoid distortion.

Flexible "Rilsan" grades have been used for sheathing wires, as for example, radio and television cables, and over polyvinyl chloride or rubber for exterior or interior tele-

"Rilsan" Molded Parts
Courtesy Societe Organico

phone insulation. In all of these aspects it is used generally for its mechanical protection qualities. The excellent electrical properties of the hard grade of "Rilsan" make it suitable for use as the sole or primary insulator for windings in motors and solenoids and for aviation equipment.

Ventilators of Molded "Rilsan"
Courtesy Societe Organico

The electrical applications of "Rilsan"[3] include coating of wires, molding of electrical outlets, molded radio or other electronic components and tape for cable insulation. The resistance for a thickness of ⅛ inch, measured between two electrodes under a continuous potential difference of 1000 volts at 64°F for four days at a relative humidity of 80 per cent is 3×10^{14} ohms per centimeter. As in the case of other thermoplastic materials, insulation varies inversely with

Extrusion of "Rilsan" Film
Courtesy Societe Organico

the temperature and the curve for the phenomenon is exponential. Because of its low moisture absorbtivity, the arc resistance of "Rilsan" is among the best of any thermoplastic material. In an atmosphere of high humidity, many substances covered with an absorbed film of water will show pronounced decrease in arc resistance. The dielectric strength or the break-through potential shows the following results. In a thickness of 0.12 inch, the dielectric strength is 425 volts per mil; at 0.02 inch it is 1000 volts per mil; at 0.008 inch, it is 1450 volts per mil; and at 0.004 inch, it is 1600 volts per mil. All of the above measurements were made at 18°C. When the temperature is raised to 140°F, the dielectric strength for a thickness of 0.004 inch is 900 volts per mil.

Wire Coverings

Copper wire, 0.5 mm in diameter, insulated with a covering of 0.1 mm of "Rilsan" will have the following electrical characteristics.[3]

Behavior under current: at 2500 volts for 15 minutes, insulation equally good at 15° and 60°C

Disruptive voltage:
at 15° C—6400 volts
at 60°C—3600 volts

Insulation:
at 15°C—160 megohms/km

Available extrusion grades:
B.C.O.—rigid, translucent
B.C.2—ivory white, rigid
B.O.P.20—flexible, translucent, fair insulating properties
B.2.P.20—flexible, ivory white

Nylon-6,6, like "Rilsan," can also be extruded as a wire or cable covering.

The high abrasion resistance and strength of nylon make it more desirable for electrical wire coatings than polyethylene, vinyl resins or rubber. Nylon has recently been used on a number of commercial types of vinyl wire to impart gasoline and oil resistance. The only real drawback noted is that in thin sections weathering characteristics of nylon are not outstanding. However, they are as good as those of polyethylene, vinyl and other thermoplastics at the same thickness. As to durability, the flexing life of a wire can be increased four to six times by coating it with nylon-6,10 and about eight to twelve times by coating with nylon-6.

Future of Molding Compounds

Nylon molding compounds are assuming a more important role in the United States, even though the volume used is small compared to that of less expensive materials. However, growth may increase more rapidly in the next ten years than it has since the material first became available.

Until now, nylon has been used primarily as an engineering material, but there is evidence that broader markets will open up as experience is gained in fabricating and using nylon materials.

Nylon requires expert molding techniques. The fact that older types of nylon had a low melt viscosity and flowed too freely to be handled with simplicity and ease accounts for the modest growth in molding applications.

Three important types of nylon are now made in the United States for molding resins: nylon-6,6 trade-marked "Zytel" 101 by Du Pont, which has been the well-established compound responsible for most of the market growth; nylon-6, first developed in Europe and basically a somewhat softer material; and nylon-6,10, which is produced largely for the monofilament or bristle market and for military wire coatings.

Because of its outstanding properties, nylon will continue to enter fields of application which have been traditionally reserved for metals. Savings, on the basis of the low density of nylon (more parts can be made per pound), partially compensate for the high cost of molding resins. The fact that parts can be injection molded directly, as compared with metal fabrication techniques, involving casting or stamping, followed by secondary machining operations, also results in cost savings. The likelihood that nylon will outwear many metals provides another basis for predicting future increased use.

Price has been a deterrent to the growth of nylon. However, nylon prices decreased about 27 cents per pound in 1956, and 50 per cent in some of the injection molding grades. If this trend continues, nylon could become competitive with such metals as die cast zinc.

Practical importance must be attached to the high melt viscosity resins, such as nylon-6, which in Europe, at least, have been proved particularly useful for extrusion and large moldings. The availability of this type of nylon in the United States should give access to big new markets such as pipe and film.

A new development involving nylon-6 is the production of nylon pipe for oil field exploration in England. This pipe is now also commercially available in the United States. Studies are underway on its use in breweries, milk plants, and in the food processing industry. An advantage of the nylon pipe is that it does not impart an undesirable taste to liquids intended for human consumption. The nylon pipe can handle a number of liquid chemicals including alcohols, hydrocarbons, fats, greases, alkalis and various solvents, such as kerosene and turpentine. The temperature stability and low heat conduction of nylon make it suitable for transporting hot liquids. The pipe may be steam-cleaned or cleaned with boiling water. A number of problems are yet to be solved, but it is likely that, if the pipe can compete on a price basis, it will be able to compete on a property basis.

Clarity, strength and resistance to attack by other materials, including hydrocarbons, make nylon-6 promising for the manufacture of plastic bottles. Other possible uses are the formation of window channels, weather stripping, hardware gadgets, fixtures and mechanical components for conveying equipment. A low coefficient of friction and light weight are other properties which make nylon of interest for conveying equipment.

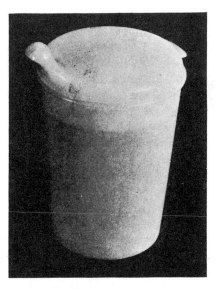

Hospital Tumbler can be colored or opaque; is unbreakable and may be sterilized. Easy to clean and bright in appearance, it is molded of nylon.
Courtesy Barrett Division, Allied Chemical and Dye

Newly developed "Plaskon" nylon 8201 has been especially designed for use in fabricating clear film and small-diameter tubing and rods. It is characterized by low moisture content and permissible temperatures of 450 to 550°F.

Since the viscosity of "Plaskon" nylon 8201 is relatively high in the molten state, it has improved moldability and minimized shrinkage in thick sections. It may also be used for fabricating bottles for aerosol spray.

Two new companies entering the nylon field are Spencer Chemical Company and Foster Grant Company. Neither is expected to have its new plant facilities in production before 1958, but both will immediately begin producing nylon in limited quantities of about a million pounds per year. These companies are introducing a modified type of nylon-6, said to be somewhat softer and more applicable for use in washers and gaskets. Since nylon-6 has a high plastic range, it is supposed to be useful for large plastic moldings and to offer new possibilities in film, sheet, and pipe manufacture. The Foster Grant Company will be especially interested in the production of nylon bottles. Competition between nylon-6 and nylon-6,6 in this country may possibly lower prices to a level where it will be economical to prepare more and more objects from nylon.

The Du Pont Company has announced an expansion in production facilities to be completed in 1957. The additional capacity will be used for producing nylon, "Zytel" No. 42. This new grade has the strength and abrasion resistance of nylon-6,6 plus a higher melt viscosity which should improve handling characteristics for molding. For this reason, it can be used in extruded products such as pipe tubing and sheeting for stamped items and post forming. It is also possible to convert the new resin into film for lamination to paper, foil, and other film.

"Zytel" 42 is especially suited for blow-molding of bottles; it produces a durable one-piece package with a mold-in color.

The amount of nylon used for nontextile applications is expected to approach 50 million pounds per year by 1960.

Thermoset Castings and Moldings

Amino-containing polyamide resins of the fluid series, "Versamid" 115 and "Versamid" 125, find widespread use in casting and laminating applications.[11] When blended with liquid epoxy resins, they harden into tough thermoset products, which are especially well suited for use in plastic tools and dies, glass fiber laminates, electrical potting and encapsulating, and general casting and molding. Pressure is not required in bringing about cure.

Selenium Rectifier Potted in "Versamid"-Epoxy Alloy
Courtesy General Mills, Inc.

When the fluid "Versamids" are blended with liquid epoxy resins, a chemical reaction occurs between the amino groups of the polyamides and the epoxy groups of the epoxy resins, resulting in the formation of a cross-linked or three-dimensional polymer.[11] The resin combinations are "two-package" systems. Blending must occur shortly before use since the resins begin to react as soon as they are combined.

Continuous mixing devices such as the Blendometer (Pyles Industries, Inc., Detroit, Michigan) or the Hardman Mixing-Metering Pump (H. V. Hardman Co., Belleville,

New Jersey) can be readily adapted to blend rapidly and efficiently fluid polyamide-liquid epoxy combinations, which are bubble-free and homogeneous.

The effect achieved can be explained by using chains to represent the epoxy and the polyamide molecules. In the case of the epoxy molecules, the chain might have a length of 35 to 40 links, whereas the polyamide molecules might have a chain length of approximately 100 to 200 links. Most common aliphatic or aromatic poly- and diamines would have a chain length of between 5 and 20 links.

TABLE 7.12. POT LIFE AND EXOTHERM OF "VERSAMID"-EPOXY BLENDS
(Ambient Temperature 75°F)

Composition	Ratio	Size of Batch	Usable Pot Life (min.)	Temp. at Gel Time (°F)	Max. Temp. Reached (°F)
"Versamid" 125:					
"Bakelite" ERL 2795	40:60	½ gal	60	185	355
"Versamid" 125:					
Ciba "Araldite" 502	30:70	½ gal	50	175	350
"Versamid" 125:					
Shell "Epon" 815	35:65	½ gal	55	195	400
"Versamid" 115:					
"Bakelite" ERL 2795	50:50	½ gal	110	140	140

When the longer chain reactive polyamides are cross-linked with the epoxy resins, a more flexible, resilient structure is obtained than that of the epoxy cross-linked with the shorter, more rigid molecules of the amine hardeners.

Typical curing cycles[5] for thin sections at various temperatures are as follows:

"Versamid" 115—Epoxy Blends	"Versamid" 125—Epoxy Blends
300°F—20 minutes*	300°F— 10 minutes*
250°F—45 minutes*	250°F— 30 minutes*
200°F—60 minutes*	200°F— 45 minutes*
150°F—80 minutes*	150°F—120 minutes*

* The time measured after the resin mixture reaches temperature.

Since the mixtures are capable of undergoing cure at low temperatures, they will have a limited useful or pot life for application, as shown in Table 7.12.

Since there is no volatile matter present and none produced during cure, the shrinkage is very low during casting and molding.[5]

LINEAR SHRINKAGE OF "VERSAMID"-EPOXY RESIN BLENDS
DURING CASTING USING OPEN TOP MOLD

Composition	Ratio	Casting Temp. °F	Shrinkage (in./in.)
"Versamid" 125: "Araldite" 6010	30:70	75	0.0003
"Versamid" 125: "Araldite" 502	30:70	75	0.0017
"Versamid" 125: "Bakelite" ERL 2774	30:70	75	0.0006
"Versamid" 125: "Bakelite" ERL 2795	40:60	75	0.0025
"Versamid" 125: ERL 2795: At. Al. Pwd.*	40:60:50	75	0.0007
"Versamid" 125: "Araldite" 6010	30:70	150	0.012
"Versamid" 125: "Bakelite" ERL 2795	30:70	150	0.014
"Versamid" 115: "Araldite" 502	40:60	300	0.0162
"Versamid" 115: "Bakelite" ERL 2795	50:50	300	0.0156
"Versamid" 125: ERL 2795: At. Al. Pwd.*	40:60:50	75	0.0007

* Atomized Aluminum Powder #101—Alcoa, Pittsburgh, Pa. and Metals Disintegrating Company, Elizabeth, N. J., or Atomized Aluminum Powder #120—Reynolds Metals Company, Louisville, Kentucky.

TABLE 7.13. PHYSICAL STRENGTH PROPERTIES OF TYPICAL "VERSAMID"-EPOXY CASTINGS

(psi)

Composition	Ratio	Compressive Yield Point[1]	Tensile Ultimate[2]	Flexural Modulus[3]	Flexural Ultimate[3]
"Versamid" 115: ERL 2795	50:50	7,300	4,600	3.0×10^5	8,300
"Versamid" 115: "Araldite" 502	40:60	6,600	5,300	1.4×10^5	8,200
"Versamid" 115: "Araldite" 6010	45:55	12,000	5,700	2.3×10^5	9,300
"Versamid" 125: ERL 2795	40:60	9,100	6,600	2.5×10^5	12,300
"Versamid" 125: "Epon" 820	35:65	12,000	9,200	—	14,000
"Versamid" 125: "Epi Rez" 510	40:60	11,200	8,000	2.5×10^5	13,200
"Versamid" 125: "Epon" 815	35:65	10,300	7,800	—	11,350

[1] ASTM D695-52T
[2] ASTM D638-52T
[3] ASTM D790-49T

Plastic Tools

Cast products are extremely tough and resistant to impact. Alone, or with suitable reinforcement and/or fillers, these compositions are used for tools, jigs, fixtures, forming dies, draw dies, surfacing dies, patterns, master models, and other similar items.

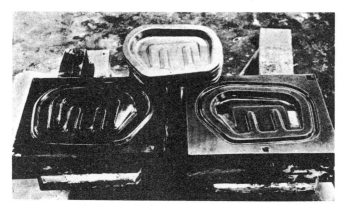

Sheet Metal Parts Formed With Plastic Dies Cast from Blend of "Versamid" Polyamide and Epoxy Resins
Courtesy General Mills, Inc.

"Versamid"-epoxy resin compositions are especially suited for die core fabrication because of low shrinkage, high dimensional stability, excellent adhesion, outstanding toughness, low exotherm and low cost. Relatively large masses can be mixed and cured at one time. Table 7.13 gives strength properties of the castings.

Soft castings are used for resilient drop hammer dies, soft hydroform dies, and soft articles. For example, blends of 60 parts "Versamid" to 40 parts epoxy resin have made

TYPICAL APPLICATIONS IN PLASTIC TOOLING[10]

Applications	Reasons for Using "Versamid"-Epoxy Blend
Master models	"Versamid"-epoxy blends are used because of their extreme dimensional stability and ability to be poured or cast in large sections without fear of excessive exotherm. They have excellent machinability, may be worked with either wood or metal working tools and may be held to close tolerances.
Checking fixtures	"Versamid"-epoxy blends have excellent dimensional stability.
Draw dies	The excellent impact resistance and ease of casting in large sections are attractive factors.
Vise jaws and chuck jaws	Castability, lack of shrinkage and ease of machining are important considerations.
Spinning dies	When pouring a large mass of resin at one time, little shrinkage is encountered and dimensional stability is more than adequate.
Drop hammer die facings	Using an excess of "Versamid" over epoxy in the blend, drop hammer die facings of great resilience and toughness are obtained.
Stretch dies	Stretch dies are fabricated from "Versamid"-epoxy blends because of the ease of casting and toughness.
Drill jigs	Drill jigs have been fabricated because of the excellent dimensional stability and the great adhesive characterstics which bind drill jig bushings firmly in place to close tolerances.
Trim and routing fixtures	The ability to reproduce detail and to cling tenaciously to metal inserts have been utilized in the fabrication of trim and routing fixtures.
Putty, plastic solders and fairing compounds	In these applications, adhesive characteristics, thermal shock resistance, mechanical shock resistance, machinability and general toughness are of importance.

excellent resilient drop hammer dies and die facings. The ratio may be varied from 50:50 to 65:35 depending on the nature of the desired product. See Table 7.14.

TABLE 7.14. SOFT, FLEXIBLE "VERSAMID"-EPOXY FORMULATIONS

Composition	Ratio	Hardness Barcol*	Shore Durometer A
"Versamid" 125: "Bakelite" ERL 2795	40:60	60-65	—
"Versamid" 125: "Bakelite" ERL 2795	50:50	20-25	—
"Versamid" 125: "Bakelite" ERL 2795	60:40	—	90
"Versamid" 125: "Bakelite" ERL 2795	65:35	—	85
"Versamid" 125: "Bakelite" ERL 2795	70:30	—	50
"Versamid" 125: "Bakelite" ERL 2795	75:25	—	30
"Versamid" 125: "Bakelite" ERL 2795	80:20	—	<5

* Model GYZJ-935

Thermoset Laminates

"Versamid"-epoxy combinations are excellent for laminating glass fiber cloth, mats, or roving.

Blends which have sufficient fluidity for dip tank, roller, and matched die methods of impregnation may be prepared. These blends "wet" glass fibers very readily and have excellent adhesion to the fibers.

Outstanding properties include low shrinkage on curing, high structural strength, high dielectric strength, chemical resistance, corrosion resistance and excellent toughness.[5] Properties of laminates are given in Table 7.15.

The fields of application for laminating compositions include:

1. Tools and dies for the metal forming industries.
2. Radomes, honeycomb panels and air frame components in the aircraft industry.
3. Printed circuit bases.

TABLE 7.15. PHYSICAL PROPERTIES OF TYPICAL "VERSAMID"-EPOXY LAMINATES
Typical Properties of the Cured Laminates*

Resin Combination	Wt Ratio	Ultimate Flexural Strength (psi) ASTM D790-49T	Flexural Modulus of Elasticity (psi) ASTM D790-49T	T.S. (psi) ASTM D638-52T	
				80°F	250°F
"Versamid" 115 "Bakelite" ERL-2795	50 50	60,000	2.5×10^6	50,000	20,000
"Versamid" 115 Ciba "Araldite" 6020	30 40	62,000	1.7×10^6	40,000	19,000
"Versamid" 125 "Bakelite" ERL-2774	30 70	73,000	2.8×10^6	42,000	—
"Versamid" 115 Ciba "Araldite" 502	20 30	55,000	—	34,000	14,000
"Versamid" 115 "Bakelite" ERL-2774	30 40	60,000	2.5×10^6	39,000	19,000
"Versamid" 115 Shell "Epon" 828	30 70	50,000	2.5×10^6	37,000	17,000
"Versamid" 125 "Bakelite" ERL-2795	40 60	53,000	2.4×10^6	38,000	18,000
"Versamid" 115 Shell "Epon" 828** Metaphenylene diamine	200 100 7.5	48,000	—	33,000	16,000

* Barcol hardness of these laminates ranges from 80-95. Laminates are 35% resin, 65% glass (6 ply 181 Fiberglass cloth, 0.060").
** ERL 2774 or Araldite 6010 may be substituted for the Epon 828 in this formulation.

TABLE 7.16. TYPICAL ELECTRICAL PROPERTIES OF "VERSAMID"-EPOXY COMBINATIONS

Property	Test Method	Condition	Laminates (approx. 60% 6-ply glass cloth, 0.06 inches thick)	Castings
Dielectric Constant	ASTM D150-47T	73°F 60 cycles	4.39	3.2
		73°F 1 mc	4.21	3.2
Power Factor	ASTM D150-47T	73°F 1000 cycles	—	0.025
		73°F 1 mc	0.013	0.015
Dielectric Strength*	ASTM D149-44	73°F 60 cycles	2000 v/mil	2000 v/mil
Insulation Resistance	ASTM D257-52T	95°F 90% r.h. cond. 96 hrs.	1.45×10^{11} ohms	10^{12}-10^{14} ohms
Arc Resistance	ASTM D495-48T	73°F	135-140 sec	80 sec

* Short time procedure.

4. Glass reinforced plastic pipe for carrying crude oil and brine, for mine piping and irrigation, etc.
5. Components for automobiles, aircraft, and boats.

Electrical Uses

The resin blends may be used for embedment or encapsulation of electrical parts to prevent mechanical damage and attack by moisture, fumes or chemicals. This is fre-

TABLE 7.17. SPECIFIC ELECTRICAL PROPERTIES OF "VERSAMID"-BAKELITE ERL 2795 EPOXY CASTINGS*

	ASTM Method	V-115/ERL 2795 50/50	V-125/ERL 2795 40/60
Dielectric Strength (step-by-step v/mil) (⅛″-thick specimens)	D149	470	430
Volume Resistivity (ohm-cm)	D257-52T	1.5×10^{14}	1.1×10^{14}
Arc Resistance (sec)	D495	76	82
Power Factor			
60 Cycles	D150	0.0090	0.0085
10^3 Cycles		0.0108	0.0108
10^6 Cycles		0.0170	0.0213
Dielectric Constant			
60 Cycles	D150	3.20	3.37
10^3 Cycles		3.14	3.32
10^6 Cycles		3.01	3.08
Loss Factor			
60 Cycles	D150	0.0357	0.0285
10^3 Cycles		0.0339	0.0359
10^6 Cycles		0.0572	0.0656

Cure Schedule—Gelled at 25°F plus 3 hours at 120°C.

Test Conditions—23.6°C, 50% RH, conditioned 96 hours.

* Courtesy: Bakelite Division, Union Carbide and Carbon Corp.

quently called electrical potting. It is important that the blends have low shrinkage during cure, so that electronic tubes are not crushed and delicate instruments damaged.

The electrical properties are excellent as may be judged from data given in Tables 7.16 and 7.17.

REFERENCES

1. Adams, G. C., Paper 22T45, American Society of Tool Engineers Meeting, April 26-30, 1954.
2. Cheney, A. J., Happoldt, W. B., and Swayne, K. G., *Plastics Technology*, **2**, 22 (1956).
3. Dumon, R., *Modern Plastics, 33*, **33**, 151 (1956).
4. General Zytel Booklet, Du Pont Company (1954).
5. General Mills Technical Bulletin 11-E (1955).
6. Hopff, H., Muller, A., and Wenger, F., "Die Polyamide," Berlin, Springer Publishing Co., 1954.
7. Merry, A. A., *Iron Age*, **173**, 158 (1954).
8. *Modern Plastics*, **32** (1), 85 (1954).
9. *Modern Plastics*, **32** (12), 85 (1955).
10. Peerman, D. E., *Materials and Methods*, **44** (1), 106 (1956).
11. Riley, M. W., "Plastics Tooling," New York, Reinhold Publishing Corp., 1955.
12. Riley, M. W., *Materials and Methods*, **41** (1), 89 (1955).
13. Rilsan Technical Note 12A, Organico Company (1954).
14. Rilsan Technical Note 12B, Organico Company (1954).
15. Society of The Plastics Industry, "Plastics Engineering Handbook," New York, Reinhold Publishing Corp., 1954.
16. Stringfellow, M., *Modern Plastics*, **34** (3), 131 (1956).
17. Wall, W. C., *Product Eng.*, **21** (7), 102 (1950).

8. ADHESIVES

Polyamide resins used as adhesives generally fall into two categories—adhesives used in hot-melt form and adhesives used in solution form. In many cases a given composition may be employed in both manners.

Hot-Melt Adhesives

Hot-melt adhesives or thermoplastic cements usually consist of a blend of one or more vegetable oil-based polyamide resins (or "Versamids") with suitable modifying agents which may include other polymers and resinous materials, plasticizers and waxes. In order to have a wide range of usefulness, these resins must exhibit a good deal of adhesive strength and a certain amount of flexibility at low temperatures; for this reason, plasticizers are needed. At the same time, to prevent the adhesive from blocking or sealing at ordinary temperatures, waxy materials are frequently added. Since, by its very nature, the hot-melt adhesive or thermoplastic cement must melt at a reasonably low temperature, wax is also necessary to offset the tendency of the material to become tacky or adhesive at fairly low temperatures. Resins and other modifiers are added to the compositions to improve immediate tack, moisture vapor resistance, adhesion to certain surfaces, and to reduce costs without significantly decreasing adhesive properties. A typical hot-melt, heat-seal adhesive for packaging use might contain the following materials:

Material	Parts by Weight
"Versamid" 940	100
"Staybelite" Ester No. 10	10
Paraffin (130°F)	4
"Santicizer" 8	10

Solution Type

The solution type of adhesive usually consists of a poly-amide resin dissolved in alcohol, alcohol and water mixtures, or alcohol and hydrocarbon mixtures. The polyamide resin may be either a vegetable oil polyamide resin ("Versamid") or a modified nylon. Modified nylons sufficiently soluble to make suitable adhesive solutions are the interpolymers such as the 6,6/6,10/6-interpolymer, or the N-alkoxy modified nylons produced by the reaction of nylon with formaldehyde in the presence of alcohol.

The purpose of the solvent is to serve as a carrier and liquifier for the resin so that it may be applied to the adhering surfaces at relatively low temperature. This is done by brushing, spraying, roller coating, knife coating or other mechanical methods. Frequently thermoplastic, hot-melt adhesives are extruded as a stream of liquid and forced into the desired position in that form.

Solvent-based adhesives always contain a properly balanced solvent to give the desired rate of evaporation and satisfactory solubility at the solids content chosen; they may also contain modifying agents.

Polyamides for Adhesives

The types of polyamide resins most frequently used in adhesive compositions are "Versamids" 930, 940, 950 and 100, nylon interpolymer 6,6/6,10/6, and linear nylon poly-

Adhesive Strength Tests With Polyamide Resin Compositions
Courtesy General Mills, Inc.

mers modified by N-alkoxy methyl substitution. All of the above are thermoplastic and may be repeatedly melted and dissolved providing the proper temperatures and solvents are chosen.

Applications

Adhesives are employed for a wide range of purposes— as bookbinding adhesives[1]; as heat-seal adhesives for bread wrappers, cigarette packages, packaged soups and foods packaged in paper board boxes; and in the manufacture of corrugated fiber boxes. They are used to a great extent with flexible packaging materials including paper, glassine, cellophane, aluminum foil, and cellulose acetate films. In addition, there are leather cements, specifically shoe cements; metal cements, especially those for the side seams of tin cans; adhesives for "Mylar"; and pressure-sensitive adhesives. Compositions of various adhesives are given in the following paragraphs.[5]

Metal-to-Metal Adhesive:

> 60% "Versamid" 100
> 40% "Versamid" 900

This combination which provides an excellent metal-to-metal thermoplastic adhesive and caulking compound is extremely tough and resistant to impact. In addition to its use as a metal-to-metal adhesive, it effectively joins plastics, foils and papers. It is applied as a hot-melt adhesive.

General Purpose Low Temperature Adhesive:

> 85% "Versamid" 940
> 5% "Staybelite" Ester No. 10
> 10% Tributyl phosphate or dibutyl phthalate

This composition is especially useful as a heat-seal coating where strength retention at low temperature is required.

It can be applied either by hot-melt or solvent techniques.

Flexible Adhesive:

> 80% "Versamid" 940
> 20% "Versamid" 100

This combination has excellent adhesion to a wide variety of surfaces. It is useful where blocking resistance is not a primary concern and flexibility is important. Blends may be made and applied in hot-melt or solution form.

Delayed-Tack Adhesive:

> 70-80% "Versamid" 940
> 20-30% "Santicizer" 9

This is a very useful delayed-tack adhesive which will remain tacky up to two hours at room temperature after activation. Actually, mixtures containing from 20 to 40 per cent "Santicizer" 9 may be used. A maximum of four per cent candelilla wax may be added if reduction of the sticky or tacky period is desired.

Polyethylene Adhesive:

> 40% "Versamid" 950
> 60% "Versamid" 100

A major polyethylene manufacturer has developed and advocated the use of this composition as an adhesive for polyethylene.

Glassine and General Purpose Paper Adhesive:

> 50% "Versamid" 940
> 50% "Versamid" 950

This adhesive is especially useful for heat sealing glassine and for general heat-seal applications where low sealing temperature and a low rate of water vapor transmission is desired. Blending may be easily accomplished by melting the solid resins together or by using solvents.

Block-Resistant Adhesives:

> 85% "Versamid" 940
> 15% "Zeco Wax" 6660 (G. S. Ziegler Co.)
> or "Wax Ester 60" (Petrolite Co.)

These combinations have exceptional blocking resistance and a low sealing temperature. The wax also makes the coating more economical. They may be prepared by hot-melt blending or in solution.

Hot-Melt Low Temperature Adhesive:

> 85% "Versamid" 940
> 4% "Versamid" 900
> 2% Paraffin Wax
> 9% Dibutyl phthalate

This adhesive has superior low temperature properties but should be applied only in hot-melt form. It provides flexible bonds for paper and other packaging materials.

Other valuable properties can be obtained in addition to those resulting from the above compositions. For example, the polyamide resin may serve as an electrical insulator, as a vapor barrier, or as a greaseproofing agent. It is sometimes used to impart a glossy effect to overprint varnishes. A typical use might be to coat paper with a polyamide resin in either hot-melt or solution form; this coating will provide adequate heat and moisture sealing. The coating could be applied after the printing operation so that the maximum advantage of overprint gloss effect could be obtained.

Modified nylons used in adhesives are not only more soluble than the regular nylon-6,6 but are also more flexible. Ordinarily, high flexibility and high solubility are found together in modified nylons. These properties are particularly desirable in bookbinding adhesives.[1]

COMPOSITIONS OF BOOKBINDING ADHESIVES

(1)	Coumarone indene-phenolic resin		35%
	Resorcinol		5%
	Polyamide A*		60%
(2)	Chlorinated diphenyl		46%
	Polyamide C‡		54%
(3)	Coumarone indene-phenolic resin		45%
	Polyamide C‡		55%
(4)	Coumarone indene-phenolic resin		35%
	Polyamide B†		65%
(5)	Diamyl benzenesulfonamide		45%
	Polyamide A*		55%
(6)	Octyl phenol		45%
	Polyamide A*		55%

* Polyamide A is an interpolymer[2].
† Polyamide B is a linear polymer, modified by reaction with formaldehyde and alcohol[3].
‡ Polyamide C is an N-isobutyl sebacamide type[4].

Polyamides A, B and C are soluble to the extent of at least 15 per cent in 80 per cent ethyl alcohol.

Thermosetting Adhesives

Thermosetting adhesives may be prepared from highly branched, amino polyamide resins which contain amine end groups, thus enabling them to react with phenolic and epoxy resins. "Versamids" 100, 115, and 125 are typical of such polyamides.

Through the reaction of amino-containing polyamide resins with phenolic and epoxy resins, thermoset adhesives are obtained. These may be used with or without solvent. An appropriate blend of the polyamide resin and epoxy resin are combined thoroughly, applied to the surfaces to be joined and held in position with little or no pressure until cure has been effected at room or at elevated temperature. In the case of phenolic/polyamide resin adhesives it is necessary to use pressure during the bonding since water is a by-product of the reaction. It is also necessary that phenolic/polyamide resin compositions be cured at high temperatures (300 to 400°F).

Epoxy Alloys

Several important changes occur when polyamide resins and epoxy resins are combined to produce a thermosetting substance. First, the two resins react to produce a new substance which is different from either of the originals. In the course of this reaction, the product becomes insoluble and infusible, although it may be softened to a certain extent by high temperatures and strong solvents. The adhesive has the excellent wetting characteristics of the polyamides and epoxy resins, and very great adhesive strength. At the same time, it plasticizes internally, i.e., the blend can absorb much greater impact than amine-cured epoxy resins can.

TABLE 8.1. IMPACT TESTS ON "VERSAMID"-EPOXY ADHESIVES
(ASTM D1002-49T) (MIL A-5090-B) (USAF)

Composition	Tensile Shear Before Impact (psi)	Tensile Shear After Specified Impacts*		
		40 in. lbs (psi)	60 in. lbs (psi)	80 in. lbs (psi)
"Versamid" 115: ERL 2795: "Surfex" MM (50:50:20)	2,730	2,180	2,260	2,240
"Versamid" 115: ERL 2795: "AFD" Filler (50:50:20)	3,420	2,870	2,460	2,260
"Versamid" 115: ERL 2795: Tabular Alumina (50:50:20)	3,200	3,220	3,350	2,940
"Versamid" 115: ERL 2795: Nylon Powder (50:50:20)	2,940	3,530	2,680	2,250
"Versamid" 115: ERL 2795: Atomized Aluminum Pwd #101 (50:50:50)	3,025	2,780	2,930	2,840

* Impacts were applied by placing the adhesive specimens with the center of the glue line on the anvil of a Gardner Impact Tester, and striking the joint with a ½-inch diameter spherical impresser at the specified force. 24ST Aluminum used in tests.

TABLE 8.2. ADHESION OF "VERSAMID"-EPOXY ADHESIVES
TO VARIOUS SURFACES

Composition: "Versamid" 115, ERL 2795, Tabular Alumina
(50:50:50)

Material	Tensile Shear Strength at Room Temperature (psi)
Brass (Naval)	2,100
Copper (hard)	1,340
Steel (cold rolled)	2,730
Glass	Glass fails
Paper Phenolic Laminates	Laminate fails

TABLE 8.3. PEEL STRENGTHS OF "VERSAMID"-EPOXY ADHESIVES

Adhesive Composition	Ratio	Material	Load per in. width (lbs.)
"Versamid" 115, ERL 2795	70:30	Steel to steel	15-16
"Versamid" 115, ERL 2795	50:50	Hard copper to copper	5
"Versamid" 115, ERL 2795	70:30	Hard copper to copper	8-10

TABLE 8.4. THE EFFECT OF SOLVENTS AND CHEMICALS
ON ADHESIVE COMPOSITIONS

(ASTM D1002-49-T) and (MIL A-5090-B)

Composition	Tensile Shear Before Immersion (psi)	Tensile Shear After Immersion in			
		Hydraulic Fluid (psi)	Motor Oil (SAE #10) (psi)	Aviation Gasoline (psi)	Tap Water (psi)
"Versamid" 115, "Araldite" 502, "Metronite" (40:60:20)	3,060	3,080	3,130	2,890	2,790
"Versamid" 115, ERL 2795, "AFD" Filler (50:50:20)	3,420	2,870	2,730	2,730	2,710
"Versamid" 115, ERL 2795, Nylon Powder (50:50:20)	2,940	2,760	2,760	3,060	2,880
"Versamid" 115, ERL 2795, Tabular Alumina (50:50:20)	3,200	3,170	3,250	3,270	3,170

Although rigid, such adhesives retain a certain amount of internal flexibility or resilience that enables the bearing load to be distributed over the surface which they cover. Some of the epoxy resins which may be used with amino-containing polyamides to produce these adhesive compositions are "Epon" resins 815, 820, 828, 834, 864, and 1001; "Araldites" 502, 6010, 6030, and 6071; "Epi Rez" 504 and 510; and "Bakelite" ERL 2795, 2774, and 2002.

TABLE 8.5. RESISTANCE TO ENVIRONMENTAL CONDITIONS
Composition Tested: "Versamid" 115, "Araldite" 502,
Tabular Alumina (40:60:20)

Exposed to	Ultimate Tensile Shear Before Exposure (psi) (av. of 5)	Ultimate Tensile Shear After Exposure (psi) (av. of 6)
250 hrs salt spray (MIL-A-5090-B,4.2.4)	3,130	2.050
7 days in isopropanol (MIL-A-5090-B,4.3.1.4.3)	3,200	3,000
7 days in hydrocarbon (MIL-A-5090-B,4.3.1.4.3)	3,270	3,300
7 days in hydraulic oil (MIL-A-5090-B,4.3.1.4.3)	3,160	2,770
60 hrs in weatherometer (MIL-A-8623,4.5.10)	2,440	2,680
7 days in JP4 fuel (MIL-A-5090-B,4.3.1.4.3)	2,440	2,680
30 days in tap water (MIL-A-5090-B,4.3.1.4.3)	3,130	2,600

The polyamide resins which have proved most successful are "Versamids" 115, 100, and 125. Because of its fairly high melting point and stiffness, "Versamid" 100 is almost always used in solution form, whereas "Versamids" 115 and

125 may be combined with liquid epoxy resins without solvent. Fillers may be added to improve impact resistance, temperature resistance and moisture vapor transmission effects, and at the same time lower costs without seriously damaging adhesive properties. They are frequently added to adjust the coefficient of thermal expansion.

Some typical compositions and their properties are shown in Tables 8.1 through 8.5.[7]

Variables in Thermoset Adhesives

The effects of changing resin ratios and of adding different fillers on adhesive strength are contained in Tables 8.1 through 8.5. Greatest strength is obtained by curing the adhesives at elevated temperatures although strong bonds are also formed at lower temperatures.[8]

TABLE 8.6. SOFT, FLEXIBLE "VERSAMID"-EPOXY COMPOSITIONS

Composition	Ratio	Hardness Barcol*	Shore Durometer A
"Versamid" 125, "Bakelite" ERL 2795	40:60	60-65	—
"Versamid" 125, "Bakelite" ERL 2795	50:50	20-25	—
"Versamid" 125, "Bakelite" ERL 2795	60:40	—	90
"Versamid" 125, "Bakelite" ERL 2795	65:35	—	85
"Versamid" 125, "Bakelite" ERL 2795	70:30	—	50
"Versamid" 125, "Bakelite" ERL 2795	75:25	—	30
"Versamid" 125, "Bakelite" ERL 2795	80:20	—	<5

* Barcol Impressor Model GYZJ-935.

By adjusting the ratio of "Versamid" to epoxy resin, various types of adhesives, each having different properties may be produced. When adhesives are high in "Versamid" content, they tend to show high peel strength on a wide variety of surfaces, but because of their flexible nature and ability to share the load, they are not rigid enough to be strong structural adhesives. Adhesive mixtures high in epoxy resin content will be soft too, but not as tough nor as high in peel strength as those which are high in "Versamid" content. At optimum "Versamid"-epoxy resin ratios, the adhesive will have maximum tensile shear strength and will be suitable as a structural adhesive.

The effect of resin ratio on some of these properties is shown in Table 8.6. It will also be seen that hardness is a function of resin ratio, as is the heat distortion value. Structural adhesives have a wide range of uses and certain limitations. They may be applied to a great many surfaces including plastics, metals, wood, paper, ceramic, and masonry. They will bond at temperatures ranging from 50°F to 400°F. At the higher temperatures the bond is formed much more quickly than at lower temperature. After curing, they resist temperatures as low as −70°F and will retain as much or more strength at that temperature than they have at room temperature. They resist strong impact, bending, thermal shock, and submersion in fuel oil, salt water, and various solvents and chemicals. See Tables 8.1 to 8.7. However, they are not recommended where high temperatures are to be encountered, as temperatures of about 250°F tend to make the adhesive soft, especially on long exposure, and when soft it loses its structural strength. The reference here is not to bonding or adhesive ability but rather to cohesive strength. However, the effect of heat need not be taken into consideration where peel strength, not structural strength, is required. When cooled the adhesive recovers its structural strength. Such characteristics may be noted in dip soldering tests with printed circuit boards.[6]

Uses of Thermoset Adhesives

Some typical compositions of adhesives for bonding various materials are illustrated in Tables 8.1 through 8.6. These include adhesives for bonding structural aluminum for aircraft honeycomb structures, adhesives for aluminum joints in aircraft, and other general purposes; adhesives for steel, for example, in automotive fabrication; for glass fiber laminates, particularly laminates made with polyester or epoxy resins; for bonding wood, as in the manufacture or repair of chairs or wood joints; for bonding copper foil to printed circuit bases in either epoxy/glass or XXXP type paper-reinforced phenolic laminate; high peel strength adhesives for steel, as in can fabrication; adhesives for bonding cork tile to masonry and for similar jobs; for leather; for "Mylar"; and for bonding other plastic materials to various kinds of surfaces. Frequently it is necessary to test various compositions when seeking optimum performance for a specific application.

When bonding dissimilar surfaces or materials, it is important to choose a "Versamid"/epoxy adhesive because of its cohesive strength and strong wetting action. The epoxy resin contains one type of polar group and the "Versamid" resin another; the combination of the two resins wets and adheres to many types of surfaces to which either alone probably would not show as great bonding strength.

To obtain the most serviceable bond, the surfaces to be joined should be thoroughly cleaned and smooth. This can be accomplished by light sanding in the cases of metal, wood, and certain plastics, or by chemical pre-treatment, i.e., chromate etching of aluminum and bright dipping or other chemical treatment of copper surfaces.

The adhesive layer must be thin (about a fraction of a mil) to secure maximum strength. This can be accomplished by applying enough force to squeeze the excess adhesive out of the joint, although pressure is not required to obtain reaction or adhesion, since there is no by-product of the reaction here or release of volatile material, providing solvent is not used. The adhesive joint will set and form a strong bond without added pressure or heat.

Phenolic-Resin Alloys

Amino-containing "Versamid" polyamide resins may also be combined with certain types of phenolic resins. In this reaction, it is believed that the amino groups of the polyamide react with the methylol groups of the phenolic resin to form new carbon-nitrogen bonds and eliminate water as a by-product, thus releasing volatile material. Temperatures in the range of 300 to 400°F are needed to bring about cure.

"Versamid"/phenolic adhesives differ from "Versamid"/ epoxy adhesives in the following respects: the former have a long pot life and may be considered a one-package system, they require high temperatures for cure, they release water as a by-product, and they require considerable pressure to form a strong joint between two materials; the latter have a limited pot life, cure at room or elevated temperatures, do not release a by-product or volatile material, and will form a strong joint without added pressure.

Before applying the "Versamid"/phenolic adhesive the joint should be thoroughly cleaned. The parts to which the adhesive has been applied should be pressed together with pressure in the order of 200 psi or higher and heated to a temperature of 300 to 400°F. At 400°F about fifteen minutes are required for cure, whereas at 300°F, about one hour is required. At the end of the curing period the bonded materials are cooled before the pressure which holds them together is released. Such bonds are much less brittle and have much better impact resistance than those made with a straight phenolic resin.

While "Versamid"/phenolic adhesives do not have the initially high strength of "Versamid"/epoxy adhesives, they do retain their strength better at elevated temperatures, so that at 250°F, it is approximately two-thirds of what it was at 75°F. They are also strong at low temperatures although they tend to be a bit more brittle than "Versamid"/epoxy adhesives. Here, again, fillers may be added as desired and can bring about various improvements, as previously discussed. The heat-reactive phenolic resins to which this reaction applies are normally all supplied in solution, usually alcoholic in nature. Since the "Versamids" are also soluble in alcohols, the two resins can be blended in alcohol or other solvent combinations. Some of the phenolic resins are not stable for long unless refrigerated, although blends of the same phenolic resins and the polyamides seem to show greater stability when stored.

TABLE 8.7. "VERSAMID"-PHENOLIC RESIN STRUCTURAL ADHESIVE
(25-40% NV Solution in Isopropanol)

Composition	Tensile Shear Strength (psi) with 24ST Aluminum		Cure Schedule (min.)	
	at 75°F	at 250°F	at 400°F	at 300 F°
40% Versamid 115				
	2500	1800	15	60
60% BR-7929				

Not only may structural adhesives be formed from blends of "Versamids" and phenolic resins (see Table 8.7), but also adhesives of high peel strength by using a greater percentage of the "Versamid" resin. For example, if the resin ratio of Table 8.7 is altered to 70 per cent "Versamid" 115 and 30 per cent BR7929, an adhesive of high peel strength is obtained (under similar conditions of cure). When bonding electrolytic sheet copper to XXXP board, adhesives having peel strengths of the order of 8 to 14 pounds per inch of width are obtained. These adhesives are especially suited to printed circuits because of their strong adhesion to copper, brass, and phenolic laminate boards. For example, they are excellent for bonding copper to XXXP type of laminate. In fact, these same compositions may be used as laminating material to bond sheets of paper to outside sheets of copper in making laminates for printed circuits. A typical composition of a "Versamid"/phenolic material to be used with cotton linters paper in making laminates is:

"Versamid" 100
50 parts

"Bakelite" BR-7929
50 parts (solids basis).

The same adhesive composition may be also used for bonding copper to the upper and lower surfaces of the laminate. This can be done in one step: the paper, after being impregnated with a solution of the combined resins, and the solvent evaporated, is laid in a press with a sheet of cleaned, but otherwise untreated copper, at the top and bottom parts; the press is closed and curing is accomplished in about two hours at 300°F under a pressure of about 1000 psi. Then, the press is cooled and the laminate removed. The copper adheres strongly to both sides of board and will show peel strength values of the order of approximately 8 to 14 pounds per inch of width.[6]

REFERENCES

1. Brown, R. G. (to Du Pont), U.S. Patent 2,612,463.
2. Brubaker, M. M. (to Du Pont), U.S. Patent 2,285,009.
3. Cairns, T. L. (to Du Pont), U.S. Patent 2,430,860.
4. Carothers, W. H. (to Du Pont), U.S. Patent 2,130,523; Frosh, C. J. (to Bell Telephone), U.S. Patent 2,388,035.
5. General Mills Technical Bulletin 11-B, "Heat Seal Coatings and Adhesives."
6. NEMA Standards.
7. Peerman, D. E., Floyd, D. E. and Mitchell, W. S., *Plastics Technology,* **2** (1), 25 (1956).
8. Peerman, D. E., Floyd, D. E., and Tolberg, W., *Ind. Eng. Chem.,* **49,** 1091 (1957).

9. WATER DISPERSIONS, ORGANOSOLS, INKS

Water Dispersions

Water dispersions of polyamide resins may be prepared in a variety of ways. One method applicable to "Zytel" nylon 61 consists of dissolving the nylon resin in ethanol, adding a small amount of an emulsifying agent, and then pouring the solution into water while stirring.[5] This forms a suspension of solid particles of nylon in water containing a small amount of alcohol. Such a dispersion may be used as an adhesive.

Another method for forming a dispersion in water applies chiefly to the "Versamid" type of polyamide resin.[3] In this process, the "Versamid" is dispersed into water without an emulsifying agent other than the intrinsic effect of the polyamide as its own emulsifier. The details of this process have not yet been published.

"Versamid" resin dispersions in water called suspensoids offer several advantages over solutions or melts of the resin and make new compositions possible. They are nonflammable, do not employ expensive solvents, and may be applied without heating. Partly for these reasons, they may be applied to paper to provide heat-seal adhesive coatings, wet-stick adhesive coatings, barrier coatings (when fused), binders, and surface-treating agents.

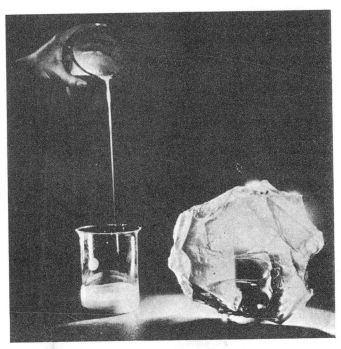

Solid Chunk of "Versamid" Polyamide Resin and of Liquid
Suspensoid Made from Resin.
Courtesy General Mills, Inc.

Water dispersions of polyamide resins ("Versamid" suspensoids) have been blended with various latices and emulsions, including rubber latices, acrylic resin emulsions, and polyvinyl acetate emulsions. Blending serves to modify the properties for the applications just described. Modification may also be brought about by incorporation of liquid plasticizers, solvents, melted resins, pigments and dyes, and thickeners.

The polyamide resin dispersions tend to hold the modifiers, strongly suspended or dispersed, as a part of the suspensoid. Dispersed solvent, for example, tends to improve adhesion to plastic films and to give a continuous rather than discontinuous coating.

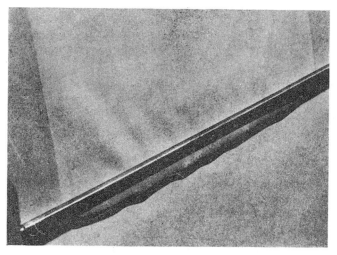

Polyamide Suspensoid Coating
Courtesy General Mills, Inc.

To minimize the tendency toward coagulation, thickening, and phase separation, pigments and dyes must be carefully selected. Pigments can be ground in plasticizers and added slowly to the polyamide suspensoid, in the form of water-dispersed slurries, or in some instances, ground directly in the suspensoid. Alcohol-soluble dyes are very effective and may be added as solutions to the suspensoid.

TABLE 9.1. PROPERTIES OF "VERSAMID" SUSPENSOIDS

Property	Suspensoid of Solid Resin	Suspensoid of Liquid Resin
Per cent solids	45	50
Viscosity at 25°C (poises)*	15-20	20 max.
Appearance (color)	opaque-white	opaque-white to light gray
Odor	very slight	slight
Pounds per gallon at 25°C	8.5	8.2
Mechanical stability	excellent	excellent
Approximate particle size (microns)	1	
pH	5 (approx.)	8 (approx.)
Acid number	3-5	6-8
Particle charge	cationic	cationic
Settling rate	negligible	negligible
Solvent tolerance	good	good

* Viscosities were determined by means of a Brookfield Viscosimeter, #2 spindle, 20 RPM, at 25°C.

TABLE 9.2. PROPERTIES OF "VERSAMID" SUSPENSOID COATINGS

Property of Coating	Coating from "Versamid" Suspensoids of Solid Resin	of Liquid Resin
Clarity	opaque-dull	clear
Color	cream	amber
Water resistance (fused state)	excellent	excellent
Blocking resistance (no block at)*	60°C/100% RH /1 psi/24 hrs	tacky
Heat sealing (°C) temperature range	90-170	
Grease and oil resistance (fused)	good	good
Burning rate	low	low
Odor	none	slight
Bond stability at 0°C to 70°C (paper to paper)	good	good

* Blocking tests carried out according to TAPPI Standard T-477-M-47. Films coated on label paper at 4 lbs per ream (500 sheets, 20 x 25 inches).

TABLE 9.3. SUSPENSOID MODIFICATION

Parts by Wt. "Versamid" Suspensoid (Solids basis)	Additive Present	Parts by Wt. of Additive (Solids basis)	Heat Seal Formation at 114°C	Heat Seal Formation at 150°C	Blocking Tests* Face to Face	Blocking Tests* Face to Back	Behavior of Seals at −29°C Passed	Behavior of Seals at −29°C Failed
100	None		No	No	No	No	0	10
0	"Elvacet" 81-900**	100	Yes	Yes	No	No	10	0
100	"Elvacet" 81-900	10	No	No	No	No	10	0
100	"Elvacet" 81-900	20	No	No	No	No	10	0
100	"Elvacet" 81-900	40	No	No	No	No	10	0
10	"Elvacet" 81-900	100	Yes	Yes	Sl.	No	10	0
20	"Elvacet" 81-900	100	Yes	Yes	No	No	10	0
40	"Elvacet" 81-900	100	Yes	Yes	No	No	10	0
100	"Elvacet" 81-900	100	Yes	No	No	No	10	0

* 50°C for 15 hours under pressure of one-half pound per square inch at low relative humidity.
** Du Pont Polyvinyl Acetate Emulsion.

Several "Versamid" polyamide resin suspensoids[4] have been studied and their properties are shown in Table 9.1 and Table 9.2.

When blended with other resins and resin latices, the combinations tend to modify each other. For example, polyamide resin suspensoids improve the water resistance and blocking resistance of polyvinyl acetate which, on the other hand, extends the heat-seal range of the polyamide. See Table 9.3.

Compatibilities

"Versamid" polyamide resins are, in general, compatible with rosin compounds and phenolic resins but not with most vinyl resins.[3] They are compatible with a wide range of plasticizer compounds but not with paraffin and microcrystalline waxes unless a coupling modifier such as a rosin derivative, compatible with both the wax and polyamide, is also present. Solubilities of these resins are given in Table 9.4, and it can be seen that alcohols of ethanol, isopropanol, butanol types along with the phenolic materials are excellent solvents for most "Versamid" polyamides.[3] Combination solvents such as alcohol and water for nylon or alcohol and aromatic hydrocarbons for the "Versamid" type of polyamide are more effective than the single solvent.

The compatibilities were obtained by melting together under a nitrogen atmosphere crushed "Versamid" 940 and the modifier in the proportions indicated. The stirred, melted mixture was observed for hot compatibility. Cold compatibility was determined by pouring the molten mixture onto glass plates and observing it after one week.

"Versamids" 930 and 940 have almost identical compatibilities. "Versamids" 900, 100, 115 and 125 are similar to "Versamid" 940 in compatibility relationships, 900 being

TABLE 9.4. SOLUBILITY OF "VERSAMIDS" 930, 940, AND 950

Solvent	Cold			Hot		
	Insoluble	Slightly Soluble	Soluble	Insoluble	Slightly Soluble	Soluble
Benzene		X				X
Toluene		X				X
Xylene		X				X
Turpentine		v. sl.			v. sl.	
V.M. & P. Naphtha	X			X		
Mineral spirits	X			X		
Cyclohexane	X				v. sl.	
Toluene-Isopropanol (7:3)			X			X
Methanol	X			swells		
Ethanol	X			swells		
Isopropanol			X			X
n-Butanol			X			X
Cyclohexanol		X				X
Ethylene glycol	X			X		
Glycerol	X			X		
Cellosolve		X				X
Butyl cellosolve		X				X
Nitrobenzene		v. sl.				X
Diethyl ether	X			X		
Ethyl acetate	X				X	
Butyl acetate	X				X	
Ethylene chloride		X			X	
Trichlorethylene		X			X	
Chloroform			X			X
Carbon tetrachloride	X				X	
Acetic acid			X			X
Acetone	X			X		
Methyl ethyl ketone	X			X		

less compatible and 100 somewhat more compatible with most modifiers than "Versamid" 940.

Organosols

Polyamide resins may be dispersed in organic solvent in the form of a colloidal suspension of small solid particles swollen with solvent but not dissolved in it. First, the resin is finely powdered with a suitable grinding or pulverizing device. In the case of "Versamid" 900 (a resin softening near 180°C and made from vegetable oil acids), a Rietz Disintegrater Mill is quite suitable. Once pulverized, the solid particles are blended with the solvent, a mixture containing approximately 90 per cent aliphatic hydrocarbons and 10 per cent butanol or "Cellosolve." The solvent and the pulverized resin are placed in a ball mill and ground for a period of from 8 to 16 hours. Addition of a small amount of wetting agent, such as lecithin, aids the grinding process. During milling, the particles are further reduced in size and become swollen with solvent. The result is a uniform thixotropic dispersion of tiny, swollen particles in solvent, which shows little tendency to flow when at rest, but flows readily when stirred. The greater the speed of stirring, the more fluid the material appears to be. By adding large amounts of polar solvents, these dispersions become nonthixotropic. Addition of weak solvents, such as mineral spirits, has no noticeable effect other than dilution. However, if a large amount of strong solvent is used in the grinding operation, a thick, viscous mush of partially dissolved resin and resin particles results. If too much weak solvent is used in forming the organosol or dispersion in the ball milling process, the product will be lumpy, grainy, nonhomogeneous and of poorly dispersed character. Many modifications of this dispersion scheme are possible. The grinding process may be shortened or lengthened, and altered by using different types of milling equipment. Pigments may be added during grinding to produce a dispersion of pigment and resin particles. Plasticizers may also be added.

A typical procedure for preparing a polyamide resin organosol[2] is given below:

(1) Granulate "Versamid" 900 to 3/16″ diameter particle size.

(2) Charge into a stone-lined pebble mill:

"Versamid" 900 (granulated)	15.0%
Mineral spirits, regular	75.0%
N-butanol	10.0%

(3) Grind 8 to 10 hours. More prolonged grinding will create excessive thixotropy.

(4) Run mill before unloading to counteract thixotropy.

The result is a more easily usable liquid form of polyamide resin, which is ordinarily difficult to handle because of its high melting point and low solubility. In the case of "Versamid" 900, the organosol is especially useful in forming films suitable as heat-seal agents. When the organosol is applied to paper, or other flexible surfaces, as a liquid film and allowed to dry, a discontinuous film of tiny resin particles is deposited. This discontinuous film may be fused by heating at a temperature of 350°F or higher. However, it serves as an excellent heat-seal film even in the unfused state and can be used over a wide temperature range. In this respect it differs from films of other polyamide resins deposited from solutions. The "Versamid" 900 organosol coating will seal in the range of 80 to 140°C. It has little or no tendency to block under ordinary circumstances, or even under fairly high pressures and at elevated temperatures. This is probably because the melting point of the resin is so high.

Miscellaneous Applications

When two or more polyamide resins of different chemical composition are combined, an interamidation reaction occurs.[1] The blend must be kept liquid to obtain a noticeable

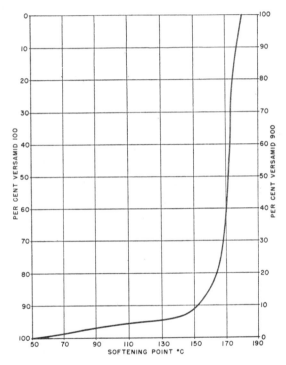

Figure 9.1. Softening Points of Mixtures of Versamids 100 and 900.

result. Normally the reaction will require heating at a temperature of between 150 and 300°C, and it may be accelerated by adding a small amount of an acidic substance. In the course of the reaction, the resins exchange acid and amino groups, and at first tend to form a block polymer with large segments of one type of composition combined with a large segment of the other. However, as the reaction pro-

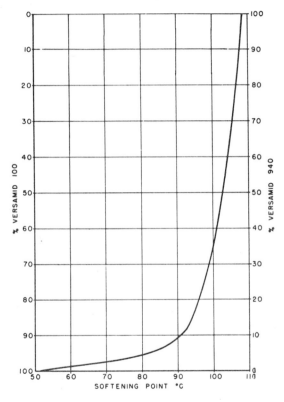

Figure 9.2. Softening Points of Mixtures of Versamids 100 and 940.

ceeds and heating continues, the segments decrease in size, eventually forming a random co-polymer. Such a co-polymer may be formed more rapidly in one step with the same ingredients. The length of time required by the mixture to reach the same equilibrium is probably dependent upon the high viscosity of the resins.

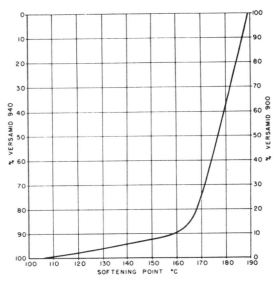

Figure 9.3. Softening Points of Mixtures of Versamids 940 and 900.

The resin blends may have some unusual physical properties. For example, a small amount of high melting resin blended with a low melting polyamide resin raises the melting point of the blend by a degree greater than would have been predicted strictly on the softening point basis. The blend sometimes shows properties intermediate between those of the component resins. For example, a soft flexible resin combined with a hard brittle resin will usually form a tough semi-solid composition. Melting point curves in Figures 9.1, 9.2, and 9.3 show the effects of this combination of resins on resin properties. In formulating cements and adhesives and in modifying softening points, use is made of these effects.

Inks

Polyamide resins, valuable ingredients in certain types of inks, may be used in spirit-soluble rotogravure inks when combined with suitable pigments and other modifying agents; these inks adhere well to paper, are tough, glossy and relatively fast drying. Because of their excellent adhesion, pigment-wetting properties, gloss characteristics, and high solubility in alcohol, polyamide resins are also used in flexographic inks. An alcohol-soluble resin is very desirable in flexographic ink compositions because alcohols do not attack the rubber rollers frequently used in such printing processes. On the other hand, these rollers are attacked by aromatic hydrocarbons, by ketones and, to some extent, by aliphatic hydrocarbons. Therefore, polyamide resins which may be dissolved in straight alcohol or in a blend of alcohol and other solvents serve especially well.

These same inks are used not only on paper but may also be applied to plastic surfaces, cellophane and polyethylene. The polar nature of the polyamide resins tends to make them adhere strongly to many types of surfaces, especially to polar surfaces. However, even though polyethylene is nonpolar, plastic material, polyamide resins adhere to it very well, either when untreated or when it has been bombarded with electrons to improve its adhesive properties.

The inks may be applied to polyethylene by flexographic printing presses with excellent results. In fact, after drying, the ink will pass the severe "Scotch"-tape test.[6]

Other types of inks may also be printed on polyethylene and those which do not adhere strongly may be locked in place by overcoating with a clear varnish composed of the polyamide resin in an alcoholic, or other type of, solvent. When the polyethylene is later fabricated into food and vegetable containers, the ink does not rub or wash off when exposed to moisture spray or handling.

Flexographic Printing on Polyethylene With Ink Made With "Versamid" Polyamide Resin.
Courtesy General Mills, Inc. and Herb Shelley Co.

The same progress that brought better ink formulations for previous press requirements brought with it a fantastic array of new press requirements for inkmakers to satisfy. Every possible range of color was demanded. High speed inks that would dry in seconds were necessary. The even, well-sized linen paper of the past was replaced by raw wood pulp with the absorbency of blotting paper.

Giant four-color lithographic presses require inks that do not smear or run between the minute dots that compose a color print, yet dry rapidly without color change. Manufacturers of leather goods, metals, glass, cellophane, paint, cloth, wood and even rubber balloons all want inks that adhere to their product and at the same time resist acids, alkalis, solvents, heat, poisonous fumes and abrasion. In addition, many different plastics, each with its own printing requirements, add to the problem. Rubbery, waxy, smooth, glossy, repellent to many fluids that touch them, these plastics are ideal for vegetable bags, bottles, packages, but require special inks.

Because the films used for most packaging are only two- or three-thousandths of an inch thick, they do not have enough "give" for smooth printing from hard metal plates. Special flexographic printing from rubber plates is preferred.

The answer to why the "Versamids" adhere so well when other resins do not is explained, in part, by the nature of adhesion itself.[6] It is believed that the forces which cause a substance such as glue, paint or ink to stick to another are the same forces that hold solids together. The strength of these forces varies from one material to another and differs between its surface and interior.

Alcohol-soluble "Versamid" polyamide resins adhere well to paper, metal foil, and many plastic surfaces, including polyethylene.

Polyamide resins are also used in other types of ink

formulas either as modifiers or as primary ingredients, but since the manufacturers of inks are somewhat secretive, little more can be said on the subject in this chapter.

REFERENCES

1. Ayers, C. W., *J. Applied Chem.*, **4**, 444 (1954).
2. General Mills Chemical Development Department Release #15-57.
3. General Mills Technical Bulletin 11-A.
4. General Mills Research Development.
5. Leekly, R. M. (to Du Pont), U.S. Patent 2,405,965.
6. Progress Thru Research, General Mills Quarterly, **10**, (4), 4 (1957).

10. FUTURE TRENDS IN POLYAMIDE RESINS

According to Hiram McCann, Editor of *Modern Plastics,* polyamides *will* be one of the important plastics of the future. One of the reasons for this is that modern plastic manufacturing methods are not yet sufficiently advanced to be able to employ many of the excellent properties of nylon—toughness, high abrasion resistance, resistance to oils and grease, and high resistance to impact. Because of these properties, nylon should find wide application in the manufacture of industrial articles and plant machinery. Mr. McCann has also stated that new processes are continually being developed which are more effective in making use of nylon. Strides have already been taken in the direction of learning to make large moldings from nylon—a difficult task. Nylon alloys, including simple thermoplastic blends of nylon resins with other resins and, more important, thermoset reaction products resulting from combinations of amino-containing polyamide resins with epoxy or heat-reactive phenolic resins, are increasing in significance.

The sales of new polyamide resins and articles and trade literature discussing them show that an intensive effort is being made to develop important uses for polyamide resins in moldings, extrusions, and coatings of various kinds, thus making it necessary to devise new types of polymers.

Trends in the future applications of polyamide resins may be determined by analyzing the primary needs of the field.

Costs and Price

In spite of their many advantages, the growth of volume production of polyamide resins has not been as rapid as that of vinyl resins and polyethylene; or it may be more accurate to say that the rate of growth of polyamide resins began levelling off more quickly. Future growth may depend on keeping down the prices of polyamides.

Since nylon compounds are now relatively expensive to produce, cheaper raw materials must be found and processing costs must be lowered. The price of raw materials used in nylon manufacture has continually been reduced, but further reduction is needed. This is particularly true of di-amino compounds used in the diamine, di-carboxylic acid condensation for linear polyamides. Although the dibasic acids are generally less expensive than the diamines used in making polyamides, it would be very desirable to lower the costs of these materials also. The dibasic acids most often used in nylon, significantly, are those having the lowest price. These are isophthalic acid, oxalic acid, adipic acid, and dimerized linoleic acid.

Long reaction period at elevated temperature and special processing are factors which make manufacturing expensive. Manufacturing short cuts, however, do not seem to be in prospect.

Resin Development

The polyamides have long been known for their sensitivity to oxidation and degradation at high temperatures, especially in the presence of ultraviolet light. Although stabilizers and oxidation inhibitors are very helpful, more work is certainly needed on improving resistance properties of polyamide resins to heat, light, and oxidation.

Another need that has been recognized for some time is related to the water sensitivity of certain polyamide resins. Because of their polar nature, many types of polyamide resins tend to absorb water readily, even at low atmospheric humidity, and thus change dimensions when the humidity of the atmosphere changes. Certain types of nylon do exist which have low moisture sensitivity and pick-up. However, new polyamides, which show greater resistance to attack by moisture and to moisture absorption, are needed.

"Rilsan" or polyamide-11, a super polymer made by the self-condensation of 11-aminoundecanoic acid, is one of the newest polyamide products of commercial significance which has appeared on the market; it is manufactured in France by the Organico Company. "Rilsan" is derived from castor oil—through a series of chemical operations the castor oil molecule is split and one portion converted to the 11-aminoundecanoic acid, which is self-polymerized by heating. Several grades of "Rilsan" polymers are made, all of which have high molecular weights, high melting points, great toughness, abrasion resistance and tensile strength, thus resembling nylon-6,6 and nylon-6,10. "Rilsan" differs from these two nylons principally in having lower moisture absorption and less tendency to change dimensions at high humidities. The electrical properties are similar to those of nylon-6,6 and nylon-6,10. For these reasons, although "Rilsan" is not as well adapted to textiles as is nylon-6,6 because of its lower melting point and lower tensile strength, it is very well adapted to making moldings, extrusions and films. The melting point, viscosity, and certain physical characteristics of "Rilsan" resemble those of the conventional plastics used in molding and extrusions, and it is not difficult to produce parts from "Rilsan" by injection molding or extrusion.

The above handling characteristics together with low moisture absorption and dimensional stability make "Rilsan" a very promising new product for fabricating such parts as gears, housings, tubular material films, bristles, and other filaments.

It may well be that "Rilsan" will be one of the polyamides of the future and of real commercial significance. The important things that may make it so are the fact that it is based upon an agricultural raw material which is renewable and not dependent upon mineral resources. Second, its properties have been adapted so as to offer advantages over super polyamides commercially available in the past. And third, its properties are such that it can be handled by existing equipment without difficulty.

"Versamid" polyamide resins are also based on a renewable agricultural product and are not dependent upon mineral resources. The "Versamids" are made from polymerized vegetable oil fatty acids which may be obtained from soybean oil, linseed oil, cottonseed oil or other vegetable oils containing dienoic fatty acids.

"Versamids," too, are being developed for use in fields where conventional nylons were little known. Because they are generally soluble in some of the common organic solvents and because they are lower melting than most nylons, "Versamids" have many interesting applications.

"Versamid" polyamide resins may be used in liquid form, as solutions or hot melts, in coating formulas, in adhesives and cements, in inks and lacquers, and in many other such liquid compositions. Liquid "Versamids" may be combined or "alloyed" with the epoxy resins or with heat-reactive phenolic resins to make new, thermoset compositions which are used to produce tough, chemically resistant coatings and strong adhesives for structural bonding uses. They may also be cast into plastic tools or reinforced with glass fibers for fabricating boats, special tools, pipe, printed circuit bases, and many structural items.

Molding Compounds

The new polymers which seem especially suited for use in moldings and extrusions are those based on polymers developed from 11-aminoundecanoic acid, from copolymers of dibasic acids combined with diamines and, in some cases, additional caprolactam, as well as from polymers developed by copolymerization of caprolactam with other polyamide-forming intermediates. For moldings and extrusions, polymers with less rigidity and more elasticity are needed than the common types, such as nylon-6, nylon-6,6 and nylon-6,10. It has been shown in previous chapters that modified polyamides and copolymer polyamide resins have these general characteristics, thus accounting for the trend in the direction of their development.

There are many reasons why nylon has been specified in place of metal for gears and bearings or other mechanical parts. In many cases it is simply replacement on cost basis alone, providing two requirements are satisfied: a reasonably large number of parts will be needed so that whatever is invested in the mold can be distributed over many pieces; and the parts will be quite complex, requiring a good deal of fabrication. It is, of course, possible that the part might cost more if made of nylon. However, the use of nylon often can be justified on the basis of its superior performance. Nylon parts operate more quietly than metal, with some requiring no lubrication at all. They are lightweight, strong, resistant to abrasion, and have smooth friction-free surfaces. The tolerances can generally be met by nylon, although it is sometimes sensitive to the effects of moisture and temperature. Occasionally it is necessary to machine the parts in order to meet tolerances. On the other hand, in the case of gears, the ductility of nylon permits the use of wider tolerances than would be possible with other materials. Nevertheless, molding with nylon presents many problems.

Nylons are noted for their crystallinity, high melting point (of the crystalline types) and low viscosity in a liquid state. For these reasons development of nylon for molding and extrusion has been slow in getting under way. Plastic materials commonly used for these purposes have more gradual softening ranges and in liquid form are more viscous than nylon-6,6. Established molding processes were made to fit older types of plastics.

For molding and extrusion, nylon requires special handling techniques because of its sensitivity to moisture and temperature. Progress is being made to overcome these deficiencies.

As the following figures show, use of polyamide molding compounds in the United States is still at a very low level, by comparison with certain other resin types.

Molding Compound Polymer	Millions of Pounds Used		
	1954	1955	
Polystyrene	309	386	
Phenolic Resins	176	200	
Vinyls	147	183	
Cellulosics	82	90	
Polyethylene	77	figures not available	
Urea and Melamine Resins	69	" "	"
Acrylic Resins	22	" "	"
Polyamides	17	" "	"
Alkyds	2	" "	"

Fibers

Because of the valuable properties they impart, nylon fibers are being combined with other fibers to an increasing extent. For example, nylon will improve the ravel strip strength of fabrics containing wool or other fibers. Because of its low fiber modulus and large elongation, wool seems to be strengthened almost proportionally to any percentage of nylon blended with it. Although nylon is not particularly effective in improving dimensional stability of fabrics, it is being used to increase recovery of fabrics after wrinkling. The especially outstanding property which nylon imparts to fiber blends is increased resistance to abrasion.

Like most synthetic fibers, nylon is melted by heat, but does not support combustion. Therefore, fabrics containing nylon will develop holes if a hot ash or a spark falls on them. Thus, it is important to blend nylon with natural fibers which are more resistant to the thermoplastic effect noted in the synthetic fibers.

In making fibers from nylon polymers, special heating grids, pumps and spinerettes had to be designed because the development of a fiber by extrusion of a molten polymer was new in the textile field. The pump was a particularly serious problem for it had to deliver a precise amount of polyamide to the spinerette. The only lubricant which could be used was the liquid nylon itself. Also, special nonwarping, abrasion-resistant steels were required because of the high temperature of exposure (about 285°C) and the constant passage of liquid nylon over metal. Improvement of fiber-forming techniques can be expected.

Another need in the field of polyamide resins is for fibers that can be more readily dyed with the commonly used textile dyes. This may come about through development of new types of nylons or through development of treatments for existing nylons to make them more amenable to the process of dyeing. Considerable progress has already been made but there is still room for much more.

At the beginning of the twentieth century there were perhaps half a dozen natural fibers available—cotton, wool, silk, flax, jute, and animal hairs. Now there are at least 23. The new synthetic fibers may be divided into the hydrophobic and hydrophylic groups. The hydrophylic group includes viscose rayon, acetate, "Cupra," "Aralac," "Vicara," "Ardil" and "Alginate"; the hydrophobic includes "Dacron," "Orlon," "Acralan," "Dynel," "Vinyon," nylon, "Fiberglas," vinylidene chloride, polyethylene, and X51. We can look forward to the development of new and better synthetic fibers of all kinds, including polyamide resins.

Coatings

Resin alloys are also being used in coatings, adhesives and casting materials. Such alloys must contain a liquid resin which is reactive with other polymeric materials including epoxy and phenolic resins.

The surface-coating field covers a multitude of uses, including decoration of architectural structures and wood, metal and plastic articles, protection of metal and wood structures, and improvement of frictional and handling characteristics. The use of polyamide resins in coatings is increasing. However, there is need for more types of polyamides in this field so that the special qualities which are important for other applications can be explored in the coatings field. Some of these qualities which will be extremely valuable are chemical resistance, toughness, strong adhesion, and pleasing appearance. Coating may now be done by several techniques, including hot-melt coating, solution coating, extrusion, lamination, and flame spraying.

General Growth

Although actual total production figures for the polyamide resins, especially the nylon types, have not been available, it is clear that acceptance of nylon was almost immediate and that for the first few years it was used for filaments in textiles and in brushes. Growth of use for molding, extrusions, adhesives, surface coatings, and casting compounds developed at a considerably later date. While use in textiles and filaments continues to grow, the other fields are now growing, too, at an appreciable rate.

To keep pace with the new uses, it has been necessary to develop new polymers. These polymers are more flexible and less rigid and are generally copolymers from two or more different raw materials. The development of the liquid polyamides, which contain reactive amino groups and which may be alloyed or reacted with other resin materials including epoxy resins and phenolic resins, is also new.

Polyamide resins represent one of the six fastest-growing synthetic resin types and, as can be seen in the accompanying table, growth is expected to continue, but at a rate lower than for some other resins.

TABLE 10.1. RESIN SALES—MILLIONS OF POUNDS

Type	1955	1956 (Estimated)	% Growth
Polyurethanes	5	150	2900
Epoxy resins	22	90	310
Fluorocarbon resins	2	7	250
Polyethylene	340	1100	180
Acrylic resins	50	125	150
Polyamides (non fiber)	25	50	100
All plastics	3500	6000	71

In the last twenty years the production of plastics has increased from 100 million pounds per year to three and a half billion pounds per year, and it is estimated that growth will reach the six billion pound level by 1960.

INDEX